W9-CFO-988

# Bridges Beyond

## *Fourth Grade Reader*

Compiled by Ruth K. Hobbs

**CHRISTIAN LIGHT EDUCATION**
A division of Christian Light Publications, Inc.
Harrisonburg, Virginia 22802   (540) 434-0750

BRIDGES BEYOND

Christian Light Education, a division of
Christian Light Publications, Inc., Harrisonburg, VA 22802
© 2001 by Christian Light Publications, Inc.
All Rights Reserved. Published 2001
Printed in the United States of America

10 09 08 07 06 05 04 03 02 01    5 4 3 2 1

ISBN: 0-87813-938-9

# Table of Contents

Bridges Beyond . . . . . . . . . . . . . . . . . . . . . . . . . . . . 1

To Richard From Nell . . . . . . . . . . . . . . . . . . . . . . . 3

Choosey Chick . . . . . . . . . . . . . . . . . . . . . . . . . . . . . 8

Stowaway on the Pony Express . . . . . . . . . . . . . . . . 17

To Be an Explorer . . . . . . . . . . . . . . . . . . . . . . . . . 25

    *Wilderness Rivers* . . . . . . . . . . . . . . . . . . . . . . . 35

Neighborhood Needle . . . . . . . . . . . . . . . . . . . . . . 37

    *Nature's Sewing* . . . . . . . . . . . . . . . . . . . . . . . . 44

Candle-Making Time . . . . . . . . . . . . . . . . . . . . . . 45

First Day of Partridge School . . . . . . . . . . . . . . . . 52

    *The Ant Village* . . . . . . . . . . . . . . . . . . . . . . . . 58

    *The Queer Little House* . . . . . . . . . . . . . . . . . . 59

Solly, the Seal That Couldn't Swim . . . . . . . . . . . . 61

    *Duck's Ditty* . . . . . . . . . . . . . . . . . . . . . . . . . . . 72

Snooky . . . . . . . . . . . . . . . . . . . . . . . . . . . . . . . . . 74

    *Chums* . . . . . . . . . . . . . . . . . . . . . . . . . . . . . . . 82

A Foxy Father . . . . . . . . . . . . . . . . . . . . . . . . . . . 83

If It Hadn't Been for Buster . . . . . . . . . . . . . . . . . 89

    *The Book of Nature* . . . . . . . . . . . . . . . . . . . . . 97

In Spite of Lions . . . . . . . . . . . . . . . . . . . . . . . . . 98

    *The Peaceable Kingdom* . . . . . . . . . . . . . . . . . 102

No Difference at All . . . . . . . . . . . . . . . . . . . . . . 103

What's a Fish Between Friends? . . . . . . . . . . . . . . 111

    *The Fisherman* . . . . . . . . . . . . . . . . . . . . . . . . 118

*A Boy's Song* . . . . . . . . . . . . . . . . . . . . . . . . . . . 119

No More Molasses Cookies . . . . . . . . . . . . . . . . . 120

*Bread Making* . . . . . . . . . . . . . . . . . . . . . . . . . . 130

The Best Recommendation . . . . . . . . . . . . . . . . . 132

The Surprise Package Company . . . . . . . . . . . . . . 140

*Neighboring* . . . . . . . . . . . . . . . . . . . . . . . . . . . 152

Sower, Seed, and Soil . . . . . . . . . . . . . . . . . . . . . 153

Spelling Bee to Spelling Book . . . . . . . . . . . . . . . 156

*Banananananananana* . . . . . . . . . . . . . . . . . . . 162

Long Before Tractors . . . . . . . . . . . . . . . . . . . . . 163

*Swallow Tails* . . . . . . . . . . . . . . . . . . . . . . . . . . 173

*The Cornfield* . . . . . . . . . . . . . . . . . . . . . . . . . . 174

*Farewell to the Farm* . . . . . . . . . . . . . . . . . . . . 175

*Autumn Fires* . . . . . . . . . . . . . . . . . . . . . . . . . . 176

Cabbages to Calves to Cows . . . . . . . . . . . . . . . . 177

The Mare That Heard a Voice . . . . . . . . . . . . . . . 187

*Little Horse* . . . . . . . . . . . . . . . . . . . . . . . . . . . 192

*Burro With the Long Ears* . . . . . . . . . . . . . . . . . 194

A Lesson That Stuck . . . . . . . . . . . . . . . . . . . . . 195

Will the Storks Fly Home? . . . . . . . . . . . . . . . . . 201

Mystery of the Empty Lavoir . . . . . . . . . . . . . . . 211

*Kind Words* . . . . . . . . . . . . . . . . . . . . . . . . . . . 220

*The Goatherd* . . . . . . . . . . . . . . . . . . . . . . . . . . 221

I'm the Big Sister Now . . . . . . . . . . . . . . . . . . . . 223

A Recollecting Day . . . . . . . . . . . . . . . . . . . . . . 228

*Others* . . . . . . . . . . . . . . . . . . . . . . . . . . . . . . . 235

Facing the Music . . . . . . . . . . . . . . . . . . . . . . . . . . . 236

Grandma's Memory Table . . . . . . . . . . . . . . . . . . . . 242

Not Worth a Quarrel . . . . . . . . . . . . . . . . . . . . . . . 249

**Glossary** . . . . . . . . . . . . . . . . . . . . . . . . . . . . . . . .253

# Bridges Beyond

"Dad, why did they call my new reader *Bridges Beyond?* That doesn't make sense."

"Well, I don't know exactly, Son. But stop and think about it. You know what *beyond* means, don't you?"

"I think it means something far away."

"Yes, that's about right. See, if you look out the window, you can see that the garden is beyond the swing set. Now tell me what bridges are for. What do they do?"

"I guess bridges take you across to places you couldn't get to otherwise. Or at least they make it easier to get there."

"Good. So do you think a reading book could be a bridge?"

"Yes, I guess it could. Maybe it has stories about foreign countries. You know, when you read a good story, you feel like you're right there. You could say the reader was a bridge that took you over to that country easier and quicker than if you really went."

"I think you're right. And if there was a story with a historical setting?"

"Then I guess the story would be a bridge back into another time."

"You're getting the idea, Son."

"I guess *Bridges Beyond* is a good title after all, Dad. I'm ready to cross some of those bridges and see what's beyond."

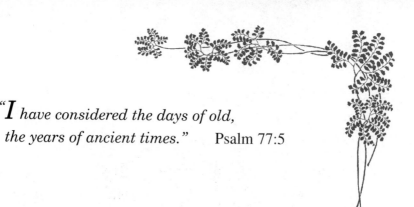

*"I have considered the days of old, the years of ancient times."* Psalm 77:5

# To Richard From Nell

Look at a map of the United States and find the states between the Mississippi[1] River, the Ohio River, and the Great Lakes. Perhaps you live in one of those states.

Before they divided this part of the country into states, it was called the Northwest Territory. (Do not confuse this with the present-day Northwest Territories in northern Canada.) People from Massachusetts,[2] New York, and other eastern states moved to the Northwest Territory and made homes there.

These travelers journeyed in covered wagons, for railroads were not being built yet. Only the brave dared to go, because of the danger of wild animals or unfriendly Indians

---

[1]Mississippi – mis ə sip′ ē
[2]Massachusetts – mas ə chü′ səts

along the way. We call these people *pioneers*. A pioneer makes a way for others to follow.

A young woman who went with her husband Henry to live in the Northwest Territory wrote the following letter to her brother—a boy in Connecticut.[3]

---
[3]Connecticut – kə net´ i kət

Dear Richard,

Although I started my day very early this morning, I am sitting up late to write this letter, for I want it to go in the mail that leaves tomorrow.

You would laugh if you could see my clay lamp. Imagine a shallow bowl filled with bear oil. A cotton wick lies in a little groove on the side of the bowl. One end of the wick lies in oil. I made the wick by twisting cotton that grew in Eliza Hardin's garden. She did not have much success with her cotton, but she did save enough for lamp wicks. We can't raise cotton here because it is too cold.

You wanted to know what kind of school we have for the children. I will be delighted to tell you all about that.

We did not find much of a school here when we came, so Henry started to see what he could do about having a better one. He said he would give a piece of ground if the other farmers would help put up the building.

The men who had children—and most of those who didn't have children—helped. Several gave logs and boards, others gave nails, and many people helped to get the ground ready and put up the building. The boat-store man gave a broom and a water bucket.

Now we have a tight, warm schoolhouse with the cracks well-**chinked.** The windows have oiled paper in them. A big fireplace almost fills one end of the room, and the benches and desks fit snugly around the other three walls of the room. On cold days the children sit on slabs of wood near the fireplace.

Elder Cox, our minister, teaches the school. He makes a fine schoolmaster. We pay him a dollar and a quarter for each child.

We had a great deal of trouble finding books. The entire neighborhood produced no more than the *Life of Washington, Robinson Crusoe, The Pilgrim's Progress,* and the Bible. We have only two real schoolbooks—*Webster's Speller* and *Dayball's Arithmetic.*

Elder Cox is a fine penman. I wish you could see the letters he makes for William to copy. We mothers make copy books of **foolscap.** We fold the sheets to make leaves and sew the leaves together. We make ink by soaking oak **galls** in vinegar.

Henry made an **inkwell** for William and Dick by cutting a section of a cow's horn and putting a flat wooden stopper in the bottom. Now all the boys have them.

Sharpened Canada goose **quills** make wonderful pens. However, it takes much time to sharpen them and keep a good supply on hand.

The children have rulers made of wood. To the end of the ruler we fasten a lead pencil made by melting lead and pouring it into a wooden mold. We drill a hole in one end of the lead to tie it to the ruler by a string. Then we sharpen the other end of the lead for writing. I wish we had some lead pencils like those you said you have in the East.

One of the nicest things the Elder teaches is good manners. The boys have to bow to the teacher when they come into the schoolroom and the girls have to **curtsy.** The boys may not wear their hats into the schoolroom. This pleases me very much. I want my sons to have good manners even though they grow up in a new, rough country.

Though Elder Cox insists on strict obedience, he seldom whips the children. The schoolmaster we had last year seemed to think doing his duty meant whipping someone every day. He had the children study aloud. You can imagine how that schoolroom sounded. Elder Cox doesn't believe in having children study in such an old-fashioned way.

The children play outside the school in the morning until the teacher comes. Then they go in and take their seats. The boys sit on one side of the room and the girls on the other, just as we used to back home. After Bible reading and prayer, the Elder says, "Books, books!" Then the students get their things in order and begin to study.

I am glad to say panthers are becoming scarcer in these parts. Any man who meets one of these dangerous animals and lives to tell about it becomes a hero to us. Our dogs help to keep them away from here. Even a small dog can frighten a panther. This is odd, because a panther could easily kill a dog, if he tried.

The wick in my lamp hardly reaches the bear oil anymore. That makes the flame sputter, so I must stop writing.

Please give my love to all the family.

Your affectionate sister,

Nell

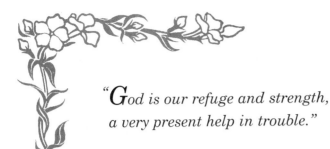

# Choosey Chick

The early morning sunlight brightened the doorway of the little cabin where Cale stood with his mother and little brother, Verygood. Cale was ready to start on the four-mile **trek** to the clearing to help Father cut trees for their new home. "Want to go along?" he asked.

Five-year-old Verygood gave an excited little bounce. "Oh, yes. May I go too, Mother?" he asked.

Mother smiled. "It's a long trek. Can you walk four miles? Yesterday you played so hard you fell asleep at the supper table. If you stay home today, Lydia and Betsy will play *Up Flies the Dove* with you when they finish the wash."

"*Up Flies the Dove*," echoed Verygood, laughing. "I like to play that. Guess I'll stay."

Then he stopped and stood thinking and frowning.

8

9

"Make up your mind, Choosey Chick," said Cale. "I must leave."

"I guess I'll go with you after all," Verygood said. "Father wants to see me."

Mother laughed merrily at the small boy's reasoning. "Run along, you two. Cale, take good care of your little brother. There's not much of a path to the new clearing. Don't get yourselves lost."

"Don't worry, Mother. I know the way. Come on, Verygood." Verygood started out happily with Cale. At the edge of the forest where the trees grew in a thick mass, he stopped and looked back. A feather of smoke curled up from the cabin chimney. He could hear the voices of Lydia and Betsy, sweet and cheerful as they sang over their washing.

"I believe I'll go back, Cale," he declared.

His brother laughed. "Well, aren't you the Choosey Chick for sure. First you want to go, then you decide to stay, then you say you will go with me, and now you changed your mind again. Go back if you want to, but don't change your mind again, for I must hurry."

Cale watched Verygood start back. Then he turned and entered the forest alone. He was disappointed that he had to make the long trek without the cheerful company of his little brother. He began to run, knowing he had already wasted too much time.

The whole family loved and enjoyed Verygood, the baby of the family. They loved his bright hair and **bonny** face.

And he almost always lived up to his name.

Father, too, was disappointed when Cale arrived at the new clearing without the little boy. The day dragged long with nothing but the sounds of their own voices and their axes ringing through the woods.

Late that Saturday afternoon they trekked tiredly into the clearing. Inside the cabin Mother straightened up from the cooking kettles. She looked beyond Father and Cale. "Where is Verygood?" she asked.

"Verygood? Isn't he here?"

All stood as still as if turned to stone. When Cale at last spoke, his voice did not sound like his own. "Verygood did not go with me, Mother. He changed his mind again when we got to the edge of the woods. I saw him start back, but I didn't watch him all the way to the house."

"I have not seen him since you left this morning," whispered Mother. She dropped the big stirring spoon into the kettle of mush and ran out into the clearing. "Verygood! Verygood!" she screamed.

Everyone ran outside, **frantically** shouting the little boy's name. The forest echoed with their cries, "Ver—re—goooood!"

Nobody thought about supper. Betsy ran through the garden, cornfield, and barn, her eyes big and frightened. Cale and Lydia searched the bank of South Fork. How dark and swift flowed the water under the overhanging branches. Father plunged into the woods, frantically shouting and firing his gun. Mother came back so weak she could do noth-

11

ing but sit on the cabin doorstep and stare at nothing.

Everyone returned when darkness fell. After a hurried bite of food, Father and Cale lit pine knots. They roamed the woods, holding the burning knots high to light their way. More than once the eyes of some animal blazed from its hiding place. Cale felt that his own eyes would burst from his head as he stared into the blackness seeking for the little brother with the bonny face and bright hair. Why hadn't he made sure Verygood really had gone back to the cabin? He should have thought that the little boy might change his mind again.

Past midnight the weary searchers gave up. They gathered around Father as he opened the Bible and read, " 'God is our refuge and strength, a very present help in trouble. Therefore will not we fear. . .' " His voice trembled. He could not go on.

The family prayed together silently, committing the youngest member to their heavenly Father.

"Keep him safe. Don't let him be scared," was all Cale could pray.

The next morning Cale thought he couldn't bear it when he woke and learned that Father had left without him. He had gone to seek help from other settlers. Only Lydia stayed at home with Mother.

"Father said we need a man at the cabin," Lydia explained. "He said you are to fire your gun three times if we receive any word about Verygood."

Staying at the cabin with everything so sorrowful and

still was the hardest thing Cale had ever done. "It's all my fault," he said to himself over and over again that long, sad Sunday.

By nightfall over a hundred men and boys had gathered. Women came bringing food and comfort.

"Oh, that I had never brought my wife and children to these wild forests!" groaned Father, as he started out again on a night-long search with the other men.

Monday morning they returned to the cabin for breakfast. Before they set forth again Father announced, "If Verygood is to be found alive, it must be today. So let us form a long line, never moving more than an arm's length from one another. In this way we shall comb every inch of the forest. We will go five miles in each direction. So young a child as Verygood surely could not travel more than five miles in this forest," he reasoned.

"Whoever finds the boy should fire three shots," suggested one of the men. "If the boy is found alive, as many as know it should fire all at once."

The line of men combed the woods eastward for five miles. Back to the starting point, then five miles west they searched. After a short rest, they started the search to the north. By this time everyone knew that darkness would fall before they could return.

The line of men stretched so far that most of them did not see the boy who came galloping up and stopped to speak to the men nearest him. But everyone heard the three shots!

Someone had found Verygood. Was he dead or alive? Cale's heart stood still. He could not breathe until he heard the great firing of guns. A thunder of shouts went down the line of searchers. Men laughed and cried with joy and clapped each other on the back.

Cale whirled and ran homeward. Others followed. Everyone wanted to tell the women the glad news. But the women had heard the shots. They came running to meet the men, Mother in the lead.

"Where is my little boy?" she cried.

"At Alvin Johns'."

"Alvin Johns!" people exclaimed. "Why, he lives seven miles away."

"True; but that is where they found him," came the answer.

"Alvin will bring him home tomorrow," said Father. "Verygood is too weak to ride this far today anymore."

How brightly shone the faces in the cabin that night! All hearts rejoiced when Father took down the Bible and read, "'I will sing of the mercies of the Lord forever. With my mouth will I make known thy faithfulness to all generations.'"

No one could do anything the next day until Alvin Johns rode into the clearing. Their bonny little Verygood sat curled in the circle of his arm.

Everyone ran out. Father reached up for his son and placed him in Mother's arms. Everyone felt like crying, but had to laugh when Verygood asked politely, "How are you feeling today, Mother?" But when he saw so many eyes on him, he hid his face on her shoulder.

Scratches and mosquito bites covered the little boy's arms and face. His legs hung thin. His clothes were torn and stained.

Of course, everyone had to hear Mr. Johns' story.

"We hadn't heard of your lost child. We could hardly believe our eyes when the weak little lad crawled into our clearing. After we fed and washed him, we tried to find out who he was. We asked him questions, and he said, 'I guess I am a choosey chick, like Cale said, 'cause after I started back to the house, I changed my mind because I knew Father wanted to see me. But I couldn't catch up with Cale. I runned and runned till I fell down. So then I tried to go home again, but I couldn't find it.'

"Verygood told us his name," Mr. Johns continued, "so then I knew he belonged to one of the Harvey families in this settlement. I sent my boy immediately to tell you we had found him. The youngster didn't want to do anything but sleep, and anyway he wasn't fit to ride seven miles on horseback yesterday. How such a little boy got that far from home, only the Lord knows!"

After everyone thanked Mr. Johns, he rode off to his home. Then the family surrounded Verygood as he sat on Mother's lap in the doorway.

"Weren't you scared?"

"Weren't you hungry?"

"Where did you sleep?" Everyone had his own question to ask.

Suddenly Verygood sat up. "When I got sleepy one time, I went in a log. D'reckly, a little black-and-white doggie crep' in with me. We slep' together and I wasn't scared any-more."

"A little black-and-white dog?" echoed Cale. He leaned over and sniffed at his little brother.

Everyone's eyes twinkled, and they tried not to laugh, for they were sure Verygood had slept with a skunk.

A deep tender light shone in Mother's eyes. "That smelly little animal knew goodness as soon as it set eyes on Verygood. It wouldn't harm a child who had no fear of it," she reasoned softly. "It must have seen his guardian angel, right there with him."

Cale, who hadn't shed a tear before this, could not help crying now. Mother had made him see their bonny, little Verygood in the great, dark woods—a little boy so tender and childlike that not even a skunk-creature would harm him. Suddenly all his ache and sorrow and guilt flowed out of him like the dark, flowing waters of South Fork. He leaped away from the steps before anyone could see his tears. With a joyous yell he turned three perfect cartwheels among the stumps of the dooryard.

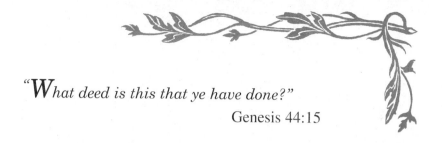

*"What deed is this that ye have done?"*

Genesis 44:15

# Stowaway on the Pony Express

Henry would never have thought of sending Polly's doll on the Pony Express if it had not been for May.

May, his little sister's best friend, had a doll that came all the way from Boston. It had a china head with beautiful yellow hair painted on in fancy wavy curls.

"Just think," May said to Polly one day, "my beautiful doll has traveled on the train all the way from Boston. Poor Betsy Ann has not traveled anywhere, has she?"

Henry saw the look on Polly's face. He saw her blink fast as she shook her head without a word.

Polly's doll, Betsy Ann, had been made by Mother out of rags. Homemade yarn hair and homemade clothes did not give Betsy Ann a fancy look at all. Polly would not dream of trading Betsy Ann for May's fancy Boston doll. But just the

17

18

same, she could think of nothing to say when her friend pointed out the **superior** qualities of a doll who had traveled.

At that minute Henry thought of a trip that Betsy Ann could take. He **resolved** that his sister's doll would do some traveling. "I will send Betsy Ann on the Pony Express," he said to himself. "She will have a much more exciting trip than poking along on a slow train from Boston. Then Polly will have something to talk about too. She won't have to blink back tears the next time May acts so superior about her doll."

Henry knew plenty about the Pony Express because at its very beginning in 1860, his older brother Joey had gotten a job as a rider. Short and slim, but strong and tough, Joey made the kind of rider the Pony Express needed.

Henry knew the Pony Express started at their home town of St. Joseph, Missouri, and ended over 1900 miles west at Sacramento, California. Since no railroad had yet been built in that part of the country, the only other way to send a letter by land was on a stagecoach. That took many weeks, while the Pony Express could get a letter to California in ten days or less.

Henry also knew that 190 stations lay spaced ten to fifteen miles apart from Missouri to California. At each station a fresh, fast horse waited, saddled and ready to go.

Joey said that when he galloped up to a station, a man ran out to take charge of the tired horse. Another one slung the mail bags onto the waiting horse. In less than a minute he took off on a run for the next station.

Of course, Joey did not carry the mail all the way to California. He rode only seventy miles or so. Then another rider took over the route, and Joey came home to rest until his next trip.

Henry knew the Pony Express riders kept traveling all night. They kept going even though it rained or sleeted or snowed. They crossed flooded rivers and high mountains. Sometimes Indians on the warpath tried to stop them. But the mail must go through.

Henry knew, too, that people wrote their letters on the thinnest paper they could find, for it cost five dollars to send a half-ounce letter. Naturally he would not send Betsy Ann that way. But he had resolved to send her another way. She would be a **stowaway** on the Pony Express.

"Joey starts his run early tomorrow morning," Henry said to himself. "I will stick Betsy Ann in one of his big coat pockets. She will have the most exciting ride a doll ever had—far more thrilling than a boring trip on a pokey old train from Boston. Then Polly will have something to brag about that will make May stop talking so smart."

So Henry made his plans without stopping to think whether his **motive** was right or wrong. That evening he found Betsy Ann. He went to the hook in the front hall where Joey's thick overcoat hung. Cold weather had come, so he knew Joey would wear the heavy, fur-lined coat. Henry pushed the rag doll to the very bottom of one deep pocket.

The next morning after Joey had left, Henry told Polly what he had done. Polly laughed delightedly. "What will Joey think when he finds Betsy Ann in his pocket? I am sure he will take good care of her. But what if he meets some Indians! That would frighten my poor Betsy Ann out of her wits. What an adventure my baby will have. Wait till I tell May."

Later Polly's friend came to play, bringing her lovely Boston doll. "Where is Betsy Ann?" she asked.

"She has gone traveling," replied Polly. She spoke very matter-of-factly as if Betsy Ann traveled every day. "I expect her back tomorrow."

"Gone traveling!" exclaimed May, in astonishment. "How could she have gone traveling? Where did she go? Did she go by train?"

21

Polly smiled sweetly. "I'll let her tell you all about it when she returns," she said, with a superior toss of her head.

Joey arrived home the next night after Polly and Henry had gone to bed. First thing in the morning they ran to the front hall. They stopped in alarm when they saw a strange coat hanging on the hook.

The minute their big brother appeared, they cried, "Joey, where is your overcoat? What did you do with Betsy Ann?"

"Betsy Ann?" repeated Joey. "I know nothing about your doll, Polly. What do you mean?"

How he laughed when he learned what his brother had done, and why he had done it. But then he said, "I'm not sure that was a good idea, Henry. Sometimes pranks like that don't turn out so well, especially when your motive is not right. Why should Polly try to make her friend feel bad?

"Anyway, Polly, your Betsy Ann will really have adventures to tell about when she gets back. When I got to my last station, it suddenly turned much colder and began to sleet. I traded coats with Ben, the next rider. He had not dressed for that kind of weather. He needed a thick, fur-lined coat like mine. So he took it and you will not see Betsy Ann until I come home the next time. I did not know I had a stowaway in my pocket or I would have brought her back."

Polly felt like crying when she thought of Betsy Ann galloping with a strange man through freezing rain farther and

22

farther from home. Henry regretted he ever thought of sending the doll traveling. He knew his motive for doing it had been wrong. What if Betsy Ann got lost! And for sure he really didn't want Polly to become a smart-acting bragger like May.

He felt no better when he heard what Polly said to May the next day. "That child of mine decided to travel farther than she first planned," said his little sister with a superior air. "And she didn't even ask me! I look for her home the end of the week, if she doesn't change her mind again."

May begged Polly to tell where Betsy Ann had gone. But his sister had resolved not to tell. She only smiled and replied, "I'll explain when she gets back."

Mother let the children stay up late the night Joey came home from his next run. He came through the door with Betsy Ann in his hand. "Safe and sound, back from her travels," he cried gaily, putting the doll into Polly's glad arms.

Henry gave a great sigh of relief when he saw Betsy Ann. How he had worried over her. But he still would not know if his prank had done more harm than good until he heard what May had to say. What if Polly bragged and started a quarrel between the little girls?

He hung around when Polly's friend came over the next day. He listened while his sister told May the whole story. They both laughed at how Betsy Ann's trip had turned out.

Then May said, "Well, Polly, your child had a more exciting trip than mine ever had. I hope mine does not get jealous."

Polly answered, "I am sure she won't, because she has traveled much further than Betsy Ann has. And a train is much more comfortable than a coat pocket." Then both girls laughed.

And Henry walked away, satisfied.

*"They go up by the mountains; they go down by the valleys unto the place which thou hast founded for them."*

Psalm 104:8

# To Be an Explorer

Ben was nearly fourteen, long-legged and strong, but he was beginning to find it hard to keep up with his father. For many weeks now he had followed the tall, lean figure in leggings and fringed hunting shirt as it moved through the woods ahead of him. Father bore a big **buckskin** robe strapped to his back. It held two extra pairs of moccasins and a small bag of **parched** corn soaked in molasses. He carried a long rifle in his hand. Ben carried a similar pack. In his hands, though, he carried only a short staff instead of a rifle.

"It is a long journey to Carolina," the boy's father had said. "If you go with me, you must do no lagging."

"I'll not lag," Ben had answered eagerly. The **prospect** of going exploring with his father made him willing to promise

25

anything. Why this was the chance of a lifetime! Ever since he could remember, he had wanted to explore beyond the narrow country where they lived. Each new day saw the Schuylkill[1] region in Pennsylvania losing more of its wilderness. New settlers built cabins. They cut down trees. They destroyed game.

"It's building up mighty thick," Father grumbled. "A man can hardly breathe."

Ben felt the same way about it. However, his mother had protested, "You should not take Ben. Such a wee lad has no business in the wilderness."

"Wee lad?" Father had asked with a grin. "Can't you see he is nearly grown? He needs to travel a while from home. He needs to get the feel of his man's legs. We own a piece of land in the Yadkin Valley in Carolina. It will take two to scout it out and tell whether it's fit for us to move there. But mind, Benny lad, if I take you instead of one of the older boys, you must play the man's part and keep a sharp eye."

Well, a good many weeks lay behind them now. Behind them lay hundreds of weary miles over ridges and around countless **windfalls** through valleys of thick timber where they crossed streams on logs.

So far, he had managed well enough and had given Father no cause to complain. However, today Ben thought Father walked faster than usual. At least his aching feet and empty stomach made it seem that way.

Many times during the morning they had sighted deer

---

[1]Schuylkill – skü′ kəl

within easy range. Father refused to risk a shot, even though they needed meat. Ben asked no questions, but he thought longingly of fresh **venison** roasted over a campfire.

Ahead of him, his father suddenly stopped. He stood beside a small stream that came tumbling down through the shadows of the woods. Ben stopped too, leaning his tired body on his staff. His body rested, but his sharp blue eyes studied every detail in the gloom of the big trees. His father tugged thoughtfully at his short beard. "Son," he said, "there are men about. They might be Indians. Keep using your eyes and tell me what you see."

Ben's searching glance swept the ground. He stooped and began to study the crushed blades of grass beside the narrow creek. Further on, he found a broken twig pressed into the hard ground. In the sand by the water's edge he saw marks that could have been made only by the toe of a sharp-pointed moccasin. Dim and faint, but signs nevertheless.

"Three men," said Ben. "They crossed the creek here nearly two hours ago, judging by the way the grass looks."

"Good," said Father. "Anything else?"

Ben scratched his head, frowning. "Yes, two of them went upstream. The other went downstream," he answered.

"What kind of Indians?" asked Father next.

"Not Cherokees," said Ben.

"How do you know?" asked his father. "You never saw a Cherokee moccasin."

Ben thought hard. Finally he said, "From the way they

27

tramped around here, they must have been lost. Cherokees wouldn't get lost in their own territory. Besides, these foot-prints look as if they came from the Tidewater. Why—why they must be white men!"

"Of course, they are white men," laughed Father. "Now why would white men come here to the edge of the Cherokee country?"

"Not to trade," said Ben. "They weren't walking heavily enough to be carrying big packs."

Father stood a moment in thought. "Beyond the high ground upstream lies the Yadkin Valley. Our land, Benny, that we have come so far to see. I will follow those two men upstream over the ridge. You slip downstream and take a look at the other man. They may be good people who got lost or they may be bad men out stirring up trouble with the Indians. When you finish scouting, follow my trail to the valley across the ridge. You will find me there. Take care, there are Indians around!"

"I know it," said Ben.

"How do you know it?" murmured Father.

"Not by any real sign," answered Ben. "I just feel it."

Father peered at him sharply. "I always said you were a born woodsman. That's why I brought you instead of the other boys."

Ben watched his father swing away into the shadows of the trees. He studied the creek several moments. Then his mouth tightened, and he started off down the bank.

He forgot his tiredness in the strange feeling of being

28

suddenly by himself in this great forest. It stretched dark and untouched around him for hundreds of miles. It held no fears for him, for he had always lived in the woods, learning to read and understand its secrets. The prospect of moving here to live excited him.

For an hour or more he followed the single trail. He moved swiftly, silently, using an Indian's care to keep himself hidden as much as possible. He knew the French and Indians had caused a great deal of trouble up north. That was one of the reasons his father wanted to move south. He wanted to leave before a real war broke out.

Suppose these three men were Frenchmen who had come south to talk the Indians into mischief against the whites. Ben stood quite still. He thought what that would mean. If someone set the Indians on the warpath, all prospects of Father bringing the family here to settle would disappear. His father would not bring his family here if there were danger of war.

Ben followed the man's footprints more easily now. He could tell by the dragging prints that the man was tired. They led away from the creek, down into a narrow hollow. From there they turned upward around a giant windfall to a ridge. Suddenly they curved back to a creek. Ben eased carefully toward the stream's edge. He knew it was a different creek, though it looked like the one he had just been on.

At twilight Ben finally caught sight of the man he had been following—a tall, well-built fellow. Certainly not a woodsman, judging by the three-cornered hat on his head.

Only gentlemen wore hats like that—gentlemen from the Tidewater, and Frenchmen from Quebec.

Ben crept silently forward. He moved like a fox from one tree trunk to another. The fellow had stopped, staring about him with a puzzled look on his pleasant, young face. Seeing no evil there, Ben stepped out from his hiding place. "How do you do, Mister Stranger? You look lost," he said.

The fellow whirled around. He blinked when he saw Ben, then smiled. "My, you startled me!" he said. "I never dreamed of meeting anyone like you in such a place!"

Ben sized up the stranger before him. Though taller than most men, the man looked only three or four years older than himself. Something about this young fellow made Ben feel friendly at once. In a few minutes they were talking like old friends.

"My name is George," said the stranger. "Don't tell me you are all alone!"

"No, I came with my father. We came down here to look at some land we own," Ben explained. "My, I am glad you are not a Frenchman."

George laughed. "We are just prospective settlers from the coast. We came to look over the land on the Yadkin, but so far we haven't found such a river. My friends went upstream to look around. They promised to return by sunset. I can't understand what has happened. Maybe if I give them a signal with the rifle—"

"No, no, don't shoot!" Ben said quickly. "We don't want to attract any Indians."

George looked his astonishment. "I have not seen an Indian for three weeks."

"Of course not," Ben said. "They would not let you see them. But they may well be watching us right now. They walk in the creeks so we can't pick up their trails. They aren't on the warpath yet, because an Indian always lets you know first. But they know white men are in their territory, and they intend to find out why."

"You seem to know a great deal," George remarked. "Maybe you can tell me what has happened to my friends, and how we can find the Yadkin."

"I'll take you to the Yadkin tomorrow," Ben promised. "We'll have to camp here tonight. Father likely has found your friends already. I hate to tell you, but you have gotten on the wrong creek."

George's mouth dropped open. Then he said, "Don't you dare tell anyone I got lost. I would never hear the last of it."

They found a well-screened hollow behind a windfall. Unrolling their packs, they made ready for the night. "I'm so hungry I could chew the bark off a tree," said Ben. "I could catch some trout in yonder creek, only I don't want to light a fire."

"I vote to take a chance on that, friend Ben," said George.

Ben stood thinking for a moment, but hunger won the victory. Opening the pouch at his belt, he took out a finely braided horsehair line with a tiny hook looped in the end. He tied the other end to a short willow switch. George watched him doubtfully while he caught a half dozen fat beetles under a log and fastened one to the hook.

"If you just had a fish spear, young fellow," he said, "I could count on you for some fish, but..."

"You just get a fire started." Ben grinned, and crept down to the creek.

George plugged the pan of his rifle and snapped the flint upon a piece of flax dusted with gun powder. When the stuff smoldered, he blew it into a flame. Soon he had a small fire burning in the hollow.

In half an hour Ben returned. He carried six large trout strung on a stick. George looked even more amazed when Ben fastened all six fish together and placed them over the hot coals to roast. But the worried frown on Ben's face puzzled him, as did the quick occasional glances the boy darted into the gloom beyond the fire.

"My friend, Ben, you seem to expect visitors," he said.

"Yes, I do," answered Ben in an unsteady voice. "D—didn't you hear them coming a while back?"

"I heard a pair of turkeys gobbling," George said.

"Well," said Ben, "that kind of turkey likes trout."

George stared at him, then rose slowly, peering into the dark beyond the fire.

"Put down your rifle," Ben whispered. "We can't run. And I won't fight."

Two tall, straight forms appeared at the edge of the firelight. Almost at once, two others appeared on the other side. Black eyes squinted down at them from coppery faces.

Ben forced himself to stand and smile into those still faces. One of the Indians wore a tuft of red feathers in his hair, and a necklace of bear claws. Only a leader would dress that way. Ben turned toward him. Raising his hand, palm outward, he said, "How!"

George, smiling, did the same thing. The leader held up his hand. A rumbling "How," came from his throat.

Ben pointed to the fish. If the Indians ate, he and George could relax. Indians never ate with enemies. If they didn't eat with them, Father could never hope to settle in Yadkin country.

In 1750, just a few years after the setting of this story, a settlement was begun on the Yadkin River. Among those who settled there were Squire Boone and his family, including his son Daniel Boone.

Suddenly, jabbering delightedly, the Indians squatted about the fire. Four pairs of hands reached out and plucked fish from the fire. Ben opened his bag of parched corn. George produced a cake of maple sugar from his pack.

"It looks like a regular picnic," he whispered to Ben.

Ben, though exhausted, lay awake long into the night. He stared dreamily beyond the figures of the sleeping Indians. He thought of the blue western mountains that he had seen that morning. What lay beyond? Well, he would find out someday soon, after his family moved here.

# Wilderness Rivers

There are rivers
That I know,
Born of ice
And melting snow,
White with rapids,
Swift to roar,
With no farms
Along their shore,
With no cattle
Come to drink
At a staid
And welcoming brink,
With no mill wheel,
Ever turning,
In that cold
Relentless churning.
Only deer
And bear and mink
At those shallows
Come to drink,

Only paddles,
Swift and light,
Flick that current
In their flight.
I have felt
My heart beat high,
Watching
With exultant eye,
Those pure rivers
Which have known
No will, no purpose
But their own.

–Elizabeth Coatsworth

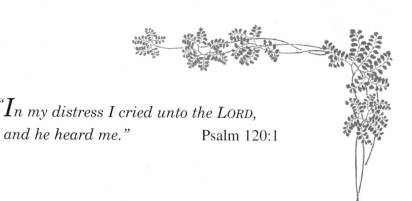

*"In my distress I cried unto the LORD,*
*and he heard me."*        Psalm 120:1

# Neighborhood Needle

More families had come westward to settle near Trader's Point. They cut more trees to make farms out of the thick forests. New log cabins stood among the stumps of the cleared acres near the Ohio River. The Sparks family, too, had cut out a farm in the new settlement.

The pioneers did all their work by hand, with each member of the family doing his share. Boys helped their fathers in the woods, the field, and barn. Girls learned to cook, spin, weave, mend, and clean. Everyone helped in the garden.

Mary Sparks was only eight, but Mother was teaching her to **darn** so that she could help do the mending for the family. First Mary practiced darning old dish towels until she could fill the holes evenly and firmly. After that, Mother said she would be allowed to darn Father's socks.

In those days few pioneer families owned needles. When a pioneer family lost or broke a needle, they could not go to a store and buy another one. They had to borrow one from a neighbor.

Darning needles, especially, were scarce. Mary's mother owned the only darning needle in the whole settlement. She gladly loaned it to anyone, and other housewives borrowed it with **gratitude.** Every time after it was returned, Mother carefully put it away in the sewing basket.

The day finally came when Mother said Mary could darn the holes in Father's socks for the first time. She ran to the sewing basket. No darning needle!

"Oh, now I remember!" said Mother. "I loaned it to Mrs. Burd last week, and she hasn't returned it. Mary, you must go and tell her that we need the needle today. She may borrow it again if she isn't finished with it."

Mary tied on her **calico** sunbonnet, put on a clean apron, and started her mile-and-a-half walk. She skipped along the shady path through the woods, singing cheerily all the way. It would be good to see her good friend Sally Burd again.

Mrs. Burd and Sally gave Mary a warm welcome, and Mrs. Burd brought out the needle at once. Before she gave it to Mary, she pushed it through a scrap of calico for safe-keeping.

"Put it in your apron pocket, child," she said. "Then you will not risk losing it. Remember it is the only darning

needle in the whole neighborhood. Thank your mother for loaning it to me. I am sorry you had to come for it, but the errand gave you an excuse to visit us. Here's a cookie to eat on the way home."

"Oh, thank you," said Mary. "I did not mind coming after the needle. I like to come to your house. Sally and I don't see each other nearly enough to suit me."

On the way home, Mary kept feeling in her pocket to make sure she had the needle. But then she forgot it for a while when she stopped to gather some wood lilies. A little further on, she laid the lilies on a log and began to pick some violets to add to her bouquet.

Before starting on, she felt in her pocket again. She drew out the calico, but the darning needle had disappeared. In sudden fear, she quickly felt all around her pocket. No darning needle. She had lost the neighborhood needle!

Mary's heart began to beat fast. She *must* find the precious needle. It must have slipped through the scrap of cloth and dropped out of her pocket when she laid the wood lilies on the log. "Oh, Lord, help me find it," she whispered.

Going back to the log, she started at one end and crawled along on her hands and knees, searching the ground anxiously for the long thin needle. At the end of the log Mary straightened up, and her eyes opened wide in fear.

A dark-haired Indian girl about her own age stood there looking down at her. Just behind the girl stood an Indian man, tall and solemn-looking. He wore buckskin leggings, and had a colorful blanket thrown across one shoulder. Mary drew back and closed her lips tightly to choke back a cry of alarm.

"How!" said the man.

Mary knew that Indian greeting. "How!" she answered in a trembling voice.

Then the Indian smiled faintly, and Mary's fear left her. The man pointed toward the oak log. He spoke questioningly in the Indian language.

The words meant nothing to Mary, but she guessed that he wondered what she had been doing. So she tried to act out what had happened. First she pretended to be sewing her apron. Next, she acted as if she were pushing the needle through the scrap of calico and placing it into her pocket. Then she turned her pocket inside out and pointed to the ground. She spread out her hands and looked back and forth, scanning the ground, to show that she could not find the needle.

The man said something to the girl, then to Mary's astonishment both Indians knelt down and began to search also. Mary joined them and all three went crawling along the log, examining the ground.

Soon the man grunted softly and held up the precious needle. Mary felt like hugging him, but she only reached for the needle with a cry of joy.

"Thank you, oh, thank you, oh, thank you, Lord," she cried, although she knew neither of the Indians understood what she said.

How could she show her gratitude? Then she noticed a three-cornered tear in the man's blanket. She tugged at it gently until he took it off his shoulder and handed it to her.

Sitting down, she spread the torn part of the blanket over her knee. She drew a long thread from one edge of the blanket. Then she threaded the precious darning needle and began to darn the tear, weaving the edges together evenly and firmly.

When she had finished, the man examined the darn, then swung the blanket over his shoulder again. He said a single word. By the pleased look in his eyes, Mary knew he meant to express his gratitude to her.

The Indian girl smiled a shy smile at Mary before the two of them took their way back into the forest.

Mary headed home. This time she clutched the thin needle in her hand all the way.

After she had put her flowers into water, she sat down to darn Father's socks. And all the while her tongue flew as busily as her fingers as she told of her adventure with the Indians.

"I'm glad you thought about mending the man's blanket," her mother told her in approval. "What would we have done if he had not found our needle?"

"The Lord knew we needed that needle," stated Mary confidently. "I believe He had those Indians turn up at the very minute I needed help."

When Father came in, he praised Mary for mending his socks so neatly. "They look almost like new," he said as he examined them. When he heard about the Indians, he, too, agreed that God had sent the Indians to help Mary.

Next day as she sat on a bench by the door cutting pieces of calico for a quilt, the same two Indians came walking into the yard. Each held out a gift: one a pair of deerskin moccasins decorated with porcupine quills; the other a finely-woven grass basket.

"What lovely gifts!" cried Mary, throwing her arms around the girl, and hugging her.

Father and Mother came out of the cabin, and the Indian showed them the neatly darned tear in his blanket.

After that the two families became good friends. Mary wore the moccasins every day. She and the Indian maid soon learned enough of each other's language so that they could talk as they played together.

Mary kept her sewing in the beautiful basket and it proved the safest place of all to keep the neighborhood darning needle.

## Nature's Sewing

If Nature ever patches
    The leaves of trees and vines,
I'm sure she does her darning
    With needles of the pines;
They're very long and slender,
    And somewhere in full view
She has her threads of cobweb
    And a thimbleful of dew.

—Author Unknown

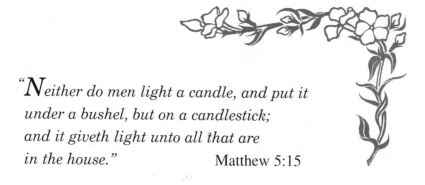

*"Neither do men light a candle, and put it
under a bushel, but on a candlestick;
and it giveth light unto all that are
in the house."* Matthew 5:15

# Candle-Making Time

Mother Turner had not made any candles since the family had come to New England. The colonists owned very few cattle and sheep the first few years in their new home, so they had little **tallow.** They could not collect enough deer fat and bear grease to make candles.

But that had changed. One fall day after Patience Turner had turned seven years old, her mother said, "We have enough tallow for candles this year. We can light our home in the same way Governor Winthrop does, although not so brightly."

"Oh, really, Mother!" cried Patience in delight. One time when she had gone with her family to town, she had seen beautiful candlesticks with snowy white candles in the windows at the Governor's **mansion.** Even the **garret** windows held a white candle. But she had never seen any candles lighted. To think of having candles like Governor Winthrop!

All the light that Patience had ever seen after darkness fell came from the burning of a big sticky pine knot. They called this knot *candlewood,* and placed it on a flat stone in a corner of the big fireplace.

They had to keep the candlewood in the fireplace so that the smoke would go up the chimney. Dirty, sticky, black drops of tar oozed out of the knot. The tar, too, must stay in the fireplace where it would burn up and do no harm to the clean room.

The burning knot made the room lighter, but it did not give enough light for reading. And Patience had always wished she could carry the light to other rooms. How nice it would be to have a light in her bedroom or to be able to check on the walnuts spread out to dry in the garret.

One clear, cold night in November, Mother said, "Tomorrow I want to dip the candles."

"Oh, Mother, may I have just one that I can carry to the other rooms?" begged Patience, "one that I can read by?"

"Yes," promised Mother, "you may have one all your own."

Patience did not have to wait until morning to see the candle-making begin. That evening her mother got the wicks ready. She stuck an old iron fork upright in the kitchen table about eight inches from the edge. Then she

threw around it half-a-dozen loops of the soft string that she called *wicking*. By cutting these loops at the edge of the table she made six wicks of the same length.

"Six, twelve, eighteen," she counted, until at last she laid out 25 dozen. "We won't have enough tallow for more than that," she said with regret. "But we should thank God that we will have better lighting than candlewood this year."

After Patience had gone to bed, her mother and grandmother continued working. Taking the wicks from the basket they twisted each one tightly, then doubled it. Next they slipped a candle rod through the loop. The candle rod was a stick not much thicker than Patience's little finger but longer than her arm. The twisted ends of wicking, when released, untwisted very little and made good, firm wicks.

Soon six wicks **dangled** by their looped ends from one candle rod. Then they began on another rod. Finally each candle rod held half a dozen wicks ready for the dipping.

When Patience saw the limp little wicks the next morning, she thought they looked like stockings that dangled from a clothesline.

After breakfast that day, Mother turned to her two tall sons. "Please build a brisk fire, boys, and bring the two big tallow kettles from the shed."

At every butchering Mother had cut off all the hard white fat from the meat. This she had saved in the shed.

After hanging the kettles on heavy iron hooks in the fireplace to melt the tallow, the boys brought in a pair of long poles. Mother placed two straight-backed chairs near the outside door. The boys placed the two poles across them. This made a kind of ladder without any rungs.

Then Mother began to place the candle rods across the poles like rungs across the ladder. "It is a good thing we made these ready last night, because the candle dipping will take all morning," she said, as she worked.

The candle rods were finally in place with their white wicks dangling. Then the boys laid boards beneath the rods to catch the greasy drippings. At last they took a kettle half full of melted tallow from the fire and set it on the hearth.

"Now she will begin to dip," Patience said to herself. But no, her mother took a pail and poured boiling water into the kettle almost to the brim.

"Oh, you spoiled the tallow," cried the little girl.

Her mother did not seem troubled. "Ask your grandmother, child; she will tell you. I cannot stop my work to explain it to you now."

When Grandmother heard Patience's question, she said, "You know fat floats on water, so the melted tallow rises to the top. Now the wicks can reach it more easily. The boiling water keeps the tallow melted. The melted tallow is deeper than the wicks are long. After your mother uses up a lot of the tallow she will need to pour in more hot water to keep it close to the top of the kettle."

All ready at last? No, not even yet. Mother opened the outside door to cool the room so the candles would harden fast. Finally she took up the first candle rod and lowered the six dangling wicks into the melted tallow.

Then Patience had another disappointment. She saw six greasy strings hanging on a rod. They didn't look at all like the white candles she had seen in the Governor's mansion.

Her mother straightened some of the wicks and laid the rod across the poles. She took up another rod and dipped it. Then another and another. At long last all fifty sets of wicks had been dipped one time.

Then she took up the first rod, with its wicks now stiff with their first coat of hardened tallow. Into the melted tallow she dipped it again. A little more tallow stuck this time, and Patience gave a small sigh. This was going to take a long, long time.

"Why doesn't she hold them in the tallow longer, so more sticks at one time? Then it wouldn't take so long," she said to Grandmother.

"Because that would melt off the tallow that has already gotten hard," her grandmother replied. "A thin layer of melted tallow will stick to the cold candle each time. But what has already hardened would melt off again if held in the hot kettle for any length of time."

After a while Mother called for the second kettle of melted tallow from its hook over the fire. The boys hung the first over the fire again and added more hard tallow. Mother poured boiling water into the second kettle and began dipping again.

So they used the kettles in turn, until at last the 25 dozen finished candles hung and swung on the rods across the poles.

Mother sat down with a sigh that somehow sounded more happy than tired. "Now as soon as they turn hard and cold, you boys can carry them to the garret to bleach."

"Oh, please, Mother, not all of them!" cried Patience. "You said I could have one."

"You are right, little daughter. Choose your candle and find Grandmother's brass candlestick. Polish it brightly and bring out the snuffer tray and snuffer. Tonight you shall see your first candle, lit and burning."

*"How excellent is thy lovingkindness, O God!
therefore the children of men put their trust
under the shadow of thy wings."* Psalm 36:7

# First Day of Partridge School

Mother Partridge led her baby chicks down the side of Taylor's Hill toward the meadow and the sparkling brook. Though only one day old, the baby partridges were already speedy little things. Their mother was taking them out for their first lessons in life. Only she could teach them what they needed to know.

Mother Partridge walked slowly, for many enemies **lurked** in the woods. From her throat came a soft cluck. It was a call to the little balls of down that came toddling after her on their tiny pink legs. They peeped softly if they discovered they were even a few inches behind. Mother Partridge watched all twelve of them. She also watched every bush and tree, the whole woods, and the sky itself.

Snakes, bobcats, coyotes, hawks—all would enjoy a tender baby partridge for dinner.

This mother constantly stayed alert for enemies, and she spotted one when she reached the edge of the wooded slope. Across the meadow she saw a fox coming toward her and her brood. In a few moments he would catch her scent in the wind. The mother partridge lost no time. By **instinct** she knew what to tell her babies.

*Krrr! Krrr!* (Hide! Hide!) she cried in a low voice. The tiny partridges, hardly bigger than acorns, also knew by instinct how to obey their mother's command. They scattered to hide. One hid under a leaf, another **scuttled** between two roots, a third crawled into a hole, and so on, until all but one had found a hiding place. This little fellow simply **squatted** on a broad, yellowish-brown chip of wood and crouched flat. He closed his eyes tightly. Now he felt safe, for he looked almost like the chip itself. One by one the little partridges stopped their frightened peeping. Not a sound would the fox hear if he came close.

Mother Partridge did not wait for the fox to reach the spot where her twelve little ones lay hidden. This brave mother flew straight toward her enemy and flung herself on the ground a few yards away. She flopped as though lame—oh, so lame—and squawked like an injured chicken.

The fox sprang at the bird. Just when he almost caught her, she floundered a foot or so out of his reach.

He followed with another jump and would have caught her this time surely, but somehow a little tree came

53

between them. The partridge dragged herself away and hid behind a log. The fox snapped his jaws and bounded over the log, but she scuttled forward and tumbled down a bank. The eager fox almost caught her tail, but, strange as it seemed, the faster he ran and leaped, the faster she seemed to tumble and flop away from him.

Amazingly, for five minutes the floundering bird had **eluded** the swift-footed fox. The faster he followed, the stronger Mother Partridge seemed to get. And always she fluttered farther away from Taylor's Hill.

After a quarter of a mile the bird suddenly rose with a whir. On strong wings she flew off to some thick bushes that lay quite a distance from the hill. The fox stared after her in bewildered amazement. Then he stalked away, disappointed and disgusted.

Soon Mother Partridge flew back to the little fuzz-balls she had left hidden in the woods. There she stood for a moment. Her children lay perfectly still. Even at her step not one of them stirred. The little fellow who squatted on the chip only closed his eyes a tiny bit tighter. Somehow they knew they must stay frozen till the mother said, *K-reet!* (Come, children!).

At once from every hiding-place scrambled a baby partridge. The wee fellow on the chip opened his eyes. With a sweet *peep, peep,* he ran to his mother. Then all the other tiny balls of down joined happily in the peeping.

To get to the water, they had to cross an open place where the hot sun blazed. So the mother spread out her tail like a fan. Her chicks gathered under it, and off they started. In this way she shaded her babies until they reached the bushes by the stream.

Here a cottontail rabbit leaped out and gave the young ones a great scare. But their mother let them know the rabbit would not harm them. That day the baby partridges learned that rabbits do not eat partridges.

They came to the brook—the purest of running water. At first the little fellows did not know how to drink. But they watched their mother and soon learned. There they stood in a row along the edge of the brook—twelve brown-and-golden balls on twenty-four pink-toed feet, with twelve golden heads bowing and drinking.

Then Mother Partridge led her brood to the meadow to a great, grassy hump that she had seen some time before. It was an ants' nest. The mother stepped on top of it, and raked it half a dozen times with her claws. The anthill broke open, and its insides scattered.

The ants swarmed out at once. Some ran around the hill, while a few of them began to carry away fat, white eggs. The old partridge, calling to her children, picked up one of these juicy-looking eggs and clucked. Then she dropped it, picked it up again, clucked, and finally swallowed it.

The young ones stood around, watching. Then one little fellow—the one that had squatted on the chip—picked up an ant egg, dropped it a few times, then swallowed it. He had learned to eat. Within twenty minutes even the smallest partridge had learned. They all had a merry time scrambling after the eggs that their mother sent rolling down the sides of the anthill. Soon every young partridge had swallowed so many eggs that he could eat no more.

Then the mother led her children upstream. On a sandy bank, well hidden by bushes, they lay all that afternoon. The cool dust running between their hot little toes felt pleasant indeed. They lay on their sides as their mother did or scratched happily with their tiny feet.

That night Mother Partridge took her little ones to a dry thicket nearby. There, under the bushes among the dead leaves, she spread her wings. At her quiet call, the babies crept under her. She covered them with her soft feathers and closed her eyes. The wee cuddling things snuggled against her warm body. They peeped in their sleep, not realizing how many things they had learned on their first day of life.

*The partridges enjoyed finding an ant village in an anthill. Have you ever seen an ant village like the one this poem describes?*

# The Ant Village

Somebody up in the rocky pasture
    Heaved the stone over.
Here are the cells and a network of furrows
    In the roots of the clover.

Hundreds of eggs lie fitted in patterns,
    Waxy and yellow.
Hundreds of ants are racing and struggling.
    One little fellow

Shoulders an egg as big as his body,
    Ready for hatching.
Darkness is best, so everyone's rushing,
    Hastily snatching

Egg after egg to the lowest tunnels.
    And suddenly, where
Confusion had been, there now is nothing.
    Ants gone. Cells bare.

—Marion Edey and Dorothy Greider

# The Queer Little House

There's a queer little house,
  And it stands in the sun.
When the good mother calls
  The children all run.
While under her roof,
  They are cozy and warm,
Though the cold wind may whistle
  And bluster and storm.

In the daytime, this queer
  Little house moves away,
And the children run after it,
  Happy and gay;
But it comes back at night,
  And the children are fed,
And tucked up to sleep
  In a soft feather bed.

This queer little house
    Has no windows or doors—
The roof has no shingles,
    The rooms have no floors—
No fireplace, chimney,
    Nor stove can you see,
Yet the children are cozy
    And warm as can be.

The story of this
    Funny house is all true,
I have seen it myself,
    And I think you have, too.
You can see it today,
    If you watch the old hen,
When her downy wings cover
    Her chickens again.

                              –Unknown

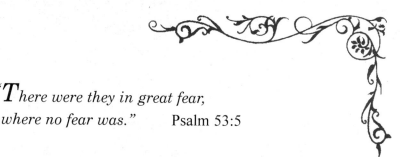

*"There were they in great fear,
where no fear was."*     Psalm 53:5

# Solly, the Seal That Couldn't Swim

On one of his exploring trips in Puget Sound[1], Clint Barlow found the sea pup. The woolly, white baby seal had lost its mother, and Clint brought it home to raise. He named it Solly. Solly never seemed to realize that he was a seal. As silly as it sounds, the sea **terrified** him, so he hadn't learned to swim.

"His mother would have taught him to swim," Daddy told Clint. "That's your job now."

Time and time again, Clint tried to coax Solly into the water, but the young seal refused to get his flippers wet.

That summer morning the three Barlows ate their breakfast in full daylight. Or was it four Barlows this morning?

---

[1]Puget Sound – pyü′ jət saünd

61

Solly stood on the porch, **supporting** himself on his flippers and peering in the window. To the family it looked almost as if he sat in a chair at the far end of the table.

Because the tides were extra low at this time of year, a new, flat stretch of wet sand had appeared in the sound that morning. Buried in the sand flats lived geoducks[2]. And geoducks invited Clint to make an **expedition.**

Clint's father got up from the table. "We should be able to finish logging that forty today," he said.

It seemed a good time for Clint to ask about the expedition. He followed Daddy out to the back porch, and watched him changing his house shoes for logger's boots.

"Dad, I think I could get some geoducks on the flats today. We won't have another low tide like this for a long time. Could I go before I do the hoeing? I can't start that anyway until the dew is off."

His father smiled as he sat on the edge of the porch lacing a boot.

"You can come up with more reasons than a lawyer, boy! Go ahead, if your mother doesn't need you." As an afterthought, he added with a chuckle, "Just don't let Solly fall overboard!"

Then he grew sober. "Really Clint, if you can't coax that pup into the water, I'll have to take him out and throw him in."

"But Dad, he's terrified of the water. Won't he drown?" protested Clint.

---

[2]geoducks – gü′ ē duks

62

"We won't know till we try. He'd probably start swimming before he drowned. Anyway, by fall he'll be too big to handle. He'll be leaving us to join the other seals. If he can't swim he won't be able to catch any food. You know what would happen then."

On their way to the beach, Clint explained his plans for the expedition to the seal. "We'll take the little skiff and row over to the flats. If you're good, I'll dig some clams for you. Just don't snort around and scare the geoducks. You never even heard of them, did you? Well, Solly, for your information, geoducks are big clams. They are **inhabitants** of our Puget Sound and a little way south of here on the Pacific Coast. Besides that, the coast of Africa is the only other place in the world you would find them."

When Clint had dragged the skiff to the water's edge, he told the seal one more thing. "You heard what Dad said about not letting you fall into the water. And about you learning to swim. Shame on you—a big seal like you being afraid of the water! We're going to have a swimming lesson at the flats. If you don't learn, Dad'll take you out and throw you into the water."

Solly wagged his head and whined.

"I hope that means you plan to try today," Clint said. "Now get in here." He tipped the skiff toward Solly, who flopped over the side.

At ordinary tides Clint had to cross half a mile of water to reach the flats. Today, though, with the extra-low tide, it looked like a whole new land had just risen from the sea. They had only half as far to row to where the flats began.

A light morning mist hung over the wet sand as Clint brought the skiff silently into the shallow water. Over his shoulder he saw the tall, shadowy shape of a great blue heron on the shore.

"Sh-h-h-h, Solly!"

The seal made enough noise at home, but now he crouched motionless in the bottom of the boat. Looking over his shoulder again, Clint saw the heron beginning to show the first signs of uneasiness. The boat scraped lightly on shells in the mud. The heron flapped into the air, disappearing into the mist.

"We've scared the inhabitants away," Clint said. "We might as well go ashore."

He stepped out into mud and water and pulled the boat up, high but not dry.

"All ashore, Solly!" He tipped the skiff for the seal. Solly looked eagerly at Clint, then doubtfully at the muddy beach.

"It's the best landing we have, Solly. All ashore!"

The seal floundered out. Clint dropped the anchor on the sand, then took up the clam shovel and bucket. They started toward the point, where the wide flats dropped off into four hundred feet of water.

"Sh-h-h-h!" said Clint suddenly.

Solly stopped beside Clint. They listened to the sound from the deep water off the point—the powerful breathing of unseen swimmers.

"Know what that is?"

Solly didn't.

"Seals."

They waited. Two sleek, dark heads appeared through the mist on the water and slid by them.

"There go some of your kin," Clint said.

Solly looked at the passing seals, but showed no interest.

"Silly seal. Just wait till fall. Daddy said you'll be plenty interested then. That's why you've got to learn to swim. You'll starve to death if you don't. No inhabitant of this sound is going to bring you fish like I do."

They went on, Clint studying the beach carefully. Clam **siphons,** level with the sand, squirted water around his feet.

Some siphon ends were big enough to be geoducks, but Clint passed them by. Wrinkled ends meant they belonged to horse clams, which are much smaller than geoducks.

Suddenly a fountain of water shot up around his foot, drenching his leg to the knee.

"Hey!" He stepped back, frowning at the smooth hole left in the sand where he had kicked aside a piece of seaweed. "That was a geoduck, Solly. That seaweed hid his siphon, and I stepped on him. Well, he's gone now. We won't dig to China for him!"

They went on more carefully and stopped near another siphon end in the sand. Instead of being wrinkled, though, it was smooth.

65

"Here's one. Now, sh-h-h-h!"

Clint went to work. He began digging only a foot away from the siphon.

Clint had not been able to find much information about geoducks' habits in books. But he had read all he could find concerning them. He knew they put their siphons up to feed and then, when alarmed, pulled them down again.

He had learned also that the geoduck has a poor sense of danger. Any activity near the end of its siphon frightens it. Then it pulls down its siphon and burrows deeper into the sand. But it pays no attention to digging and other movements a short distance away.

"See, I've got to dig down lower than where I think the clam is," he explained to the seal. "Then I can get my shovel under him from the side."

At last he stopped digging and rested, supporting himself on his shovel. "Now, Solly, we'll see if I figured right. I hope I did or Dad will say this expedition was a failure for sure."

Solly looked up from nosing a crab that he had dug out of the sand. He wagged his head as if to say, "I'm sure you figured correctly, Master."

"Wait, Solly, we haven't gotten him yet. First we go like this—" Clint began digging under the sand between the hole and the geoduck. He pushed the shovel farther and farther while keeping an eye on the siphon end.

"Sh-h-h-h. A few more inches—"

The shovel scraped on a stone. A fountain of water shot

up as the siphon end disappeared. Clint drove the shovel forward with all his strength. As it stopped, he felt something alive bump down on the steel blade.

"Got him, Solly."

Solly looked, but there wasn't much to see—just the handle of the shovel disappearing into mud and water.

With his hands Clint crumbled away the wall of sand. Soon he could see the cream-and-white shell of the big clam. He lifted it out by its foot-long siphon and raised it in the air.

"Look at that, Solly. It'll weigh five pounds."

Looking at the geoduck, Clint wondered why the big clams lived thousands of miles apart in only two small areas in the world. The books didn't say why. It seemed to Clint that someone should try to find out why the huge clam does not live at other places on the earth.

Clint went on down the beach and got several other geoducks. Then he stopped and dug some small clams, which he opened for the seal to eat.

"I'm doing this because you're my best friend, Solly. But just remember, none of your seal friends will dig clams and open them for you. That's why you must learn to swim so that you can catch your own fish."

Solly barked a thank-you, and then coaxed the boy to explore the rest of the new beach exposed by the low tide.

Clint didn't notice the passing of time. He had forgotten all about hoeing. He didn't notice that the tide had turned

until they headed back. Then he saw the skiff afloat a good way from the shore.

"Careless of us, Solly. We'll have to wade or maybe swim for it. That is, I'll swim. You wouldn't know about things like that! And now it's too late to give you a swimming lesson. That was supposed to be part of this expedition. What will Dad say?"

Clint waded out to the skiff. The water came well above his knees. He dropped the shovel over the side and set in the bucket of clams. Then he heard Solly bark. He looked back to see the seal lifting first one flipper and then the other at the edge of the rising water. He barked again as if to say, "Come and get me."

"Indeed I will not!" Clint called. "You come here!"

Solly's answer sounded as if he were saying he would go through fire for Clint. But deep water? He had to draw the line somewhere!

"Here, Solly! Come on, you silly seal!"

Then began the contest. Clint tried to get his pet to swim to the boat. The seal kept imploring Clint to come and rescue him from the incoming tide.

While he sat there begging, the tide rose about him. Now, as he raised one flipper and then the other, they sloshed in the water like paddles.

"Here, Solly! Come on, Solly! You can swim. Just try it."

The seal snorted loudly as if he had gotten water up his nose. Water swirled along his sides—almost over his back.

"Solly, here, Solly! Come on!"

Solly snorted again, and suddenly lurched forward and began moving his flippers.

Clint, standing in water to his waist, cheered. "Solly, you did it. You're swimming!"

The seal glided up to him. Clint thought he looked surprised as well as delighted. At least that's the way Clint himself felt.

"Solly, you've done it!" he repeated, a wide grin on his face. The boy could hardly believe his eyes.

His pet came close. Then with a gleam of mischief in his eyes, he ducked his head and smoothly glided away under the surface.

Clint scrambled over the stern of the skiff and pulled up the anchor. A hundred feet away, Solly's sleek head popped above the surface. Then he came swimming alongside, still wearing that surprised, delighted look.

"Here, Solly, come around to the stern, and I'll help you in."

But Solly dived out of sight. No more riding in boats for him.

Clint started to row home alone. He could hardly wait to tell Dad that Solly could swim. He felt happy for his pet, but already had begun to feel lonely. What would he do with himself the rest of the summer without the young seal? What would he do in the fall when Solly left for good?

He stopped rowing when Solly came swimming toward him, but the seal dived again. Looking down, Clint saw him speed away underwater like a flying shadow.

His pet had found his world, the world into which God had created him. Lonely, yet deeply satisfied, Clint pulled for home.

*Solly likely soon learned to find his food under the water. Here is a poem about another animal that goes under the water to find food.*

# Duck's Ditty

All along the backwater,
   Through the rushes tall,
Ducks are a-dabbling,
   Up tails all!

Ducks' tails, drakes' tails,
   Yellow feet a-quiver,
Yellow bills all out of sight
   Busy in the river!

Slushy green undergrowth
   Where the roaches swim—
Here we keep our larder,
   Cool and full and dim.

Everyone for what he likes!
  *We* like to be
Heads down, tails up,
  Dabbling free!

High in the blue above
  Swifts whirl and call—
*We* are down a-dabbling,
  Up tails all!

–Kenneth Grahame

*"**H**e casteth forth his ice like morsels: who can stand before his cold?"* Psalm 147:17

# Snooky

Bobby had raised Snooky from a pup. The big husky had played with him and slept with him. The eleven-year-old boy himself had broken his prized pet to the sled. At a year old, Snooky could pull in harness as well as any of the older dogs at the Hudson's Bay trading post in Northern Saskatchewan.

"Snooky's a keen trail dog, Son!" said Bobby's father one morning as he watched Snooky pick up the command "March!" of a driver and lead off at a steady **gait** with the dog team. "Looks as if he's ready to work."

Bobby had always known that Snooky would have to work for his keep. Somehow, though, his father's words this morning made him sad. The sled dogs worked hard. Dog drivers would use their whips as quickly on young Snooky as they did on the older dogs.

"We have plenty of dogs," said Bobby at last. "Can't Snooky have a little more time to grow up?"

"Son," said his father, "since airplanes pick up our furs now, we run tighter schedules. Snooky's mother, Fancy, and her teammate can't make long, fast trips anymore. I must put strong dog teams on the trails to reach the outposts and return more quickly. The time has come for Snooky to step into his mother's traces."

"I understand that, Father," said Bobby. "I just don't like to think of anyone else driving Snooky. Won't you let me drive him? I can manage the team okay. I know the way to the outposts, and I'd love to drive Snooky. After all, I'm going on twelve."

"I know," said Bobby's father, "but I can't risk letting you go. Things come up on the trail that you couldn't manage. It's too big a responsibility for a boy your age."

Bobby said no more. As a trapper in this rough northern country, his father faced a hard **existence.** Furs trapped in the outlying wilderness were collected at outposts, then brought by dogsled to the Hudson's Bay post. Now, with airplane service in the region, the pelts had to be brought in on schedule. Father had to make sure the furs were counted, graded, and properly packed well ahead of time. The plane would not wait.

In spite of his firm decision, Bobby's father understood the disappointment in Bobby's eyes. He said kindly, "After today, I'll give Snooky to one of my best drivers."

"Who will drive him today?" asked Bobby.

His father did not answer. Turning to his new **assistant,** he said, "Joe, I can't think why the team from the Crooked River post hasn't gotten here. Maybe the driver went around the other way. You'll have to go to Crooked River and pick up those furs if the other team doesn't bring them in by noon today."

At noon, the outfit from Crooked River had not come. Bobby heard his father tell Joe, "Hitch up a sled and start out. Put young Snooky in as lead dog. You'll hit the outpost late tonight. That should put you back here by tomorrow night."

Bobby **resisted** the idea of Joe driving his dog, for the assistant had little experience handling a dog team, although he was an experienced woodsman. However, all the regular drivers were gone.

He tried once more. "Father, please let me go! I know the trail to Crooked River post and can handle the team easily. I wouldn't have any trouble at all."

"No, Bobby," said his father. "I can't let you go. You are too young. Knowing the trail and being able to drive are only part of the responsibility. There are many other things a driver must be able to manage."

So Bobby watched Joe hitch up Snooky and the other dogs and head out for the Crooked River post. But he couldn't think of one thing he and Snooky couldn't handle together.

The next morning Bobby awoke to a blizzard driving out of the north. All day the wind whined and whipped around the Hudson's Bay post, packing the light, dry snow into every crack and corner. Drifts closed the trails.

Night came. The blizzard still howled. Joe had not come. Bobby's father paced the floor. All Bobby could think was, *I didn't think about a blizzard! What if Father had let me go? I'd be stuck out in this blizzard somewhere.*

By morning the wind had dropped. The sun shone brilliantly, but without warmth, over a dazzling white wonderland. His father soberly watched the trail for a sign of Joe. Finally he went off to examine some traplines.

Snooky! Bobby kept worrying about Snooky. He could not bring himself to do anything but watch the trail. After what seemed a long time, his eyes opened in astonishment. There, across the frozen lake, running with the steady gait peculiar to huskies, came Snooky. Without thought of the cold, Bobby ran to meet his dog.

"Snooky, what's the matter? Where is Joe? Snooky, why did you run away?" he cried, throwing his arms around Snooky's neck. "Come on. We'll find Father. Oh, Snooky, he'll whip you for running away!"

With his hand on Snooky's collar, Bobby turned to run back to the post. But Snooky caught a corner of Bobby's sweater in his teeth and refused to move.

"Come on, Snooky! Come, I say!" cried Bobby, impatiently, but Snooky resisted and kept whining and pulling at his master's sweater.

"All right, I'll come with you, then," Bobby said. "Wait till I get my coat and things." Snooky seemed to understand his words for he loosened his grip on Bobby's sweater.

Away to the cabin Bobby raced for his boots and warm outer clothes. He knew what Snooky meant. Something must have happened to Joe. Yes, something must be wrong. He raced back to Snooky, who stood on the ice waiting for him, wagging his tail in great excitement.

"Now," said Bobby, putting his hand on his dog, "let's go." Snooky turned and started off at an easy, steady pace.

The wind had swept the ice clean, making the going hard. Bobby half ran, half slid along in his smooth shoepacks. Snooky kept a straight course down the long, narrow lake with Bobby hurrying behind him.

Bobby's fur cap and snug moosehide jacket and leggings kept him warm. However, the bitter cold air stung his face. When he felt the pain leaving his nose and cheeks, he knew they were freezing. Then he stopped and buried his face in Snooky's warm coat. Snooky wagged his tail and rubbed affectionately against his friend and master.

In a few minutes they started off again. After an hour's steady going, Bobby still had seen no sign of Joe. His exposed face was beginning to freeze again. Stopping, he pulled off his mitten and rubbed his warm fist over his cheeks. "I sure am glad Father didn't let me go to the Crooked River post," he exclaimed to himself. "I could never have managed in the blizzard and this terrible cold." He called to the dog, "Snooky, you don't know what you're doing! I'm going back for Father!" he declared.

Snooky began to whimper. He braced his feet in the snow and tugged at Bobby's jacket.

"No!" Bobby refused. "I'm going back. Now, let go!"

Snooky pulled harder, and his eyes begged.

"Well," said Bobby as he looked ahead and got his bearings, "I'll go to that next hill yet. I know a trapper's cabin is on the other side. We'll rest and get out of this cold a bit. But then I am going back."

Bobby had given up hope of finding Joe. Now all he could think about was how foolish he had been to come without leaving a note. Now his father would probably think he was not responsible enough to drive a dog team.

Snooky bounded forward again at a faster gait than ever. This time Bobby found it hard to keep up with him, but he floundered after as best he could.

Just then Bobby saw a little flag waving. A flag, the trapper's signal of distress! Snooky began to run faster.

On ahead, the big dog stopped and began to bark at a piled-up heap on the snow. The pile exploded and Bobby saw the other dogs, still in harness, jumping and barking.

Bobby found Joe huddled among the furs on his sled. Exhausted and half-dazed, he lay there, one side of his face badly frozen.

"Bobby, my feet . . . frozen," Joe mumbled. ". . . no feeling . . . lost way in blizzard . . . wandering all night . . . . This morning I let Snooky loose."

"We're not far from a trapper's cabin," said Bobby.

"I'm going to go get a fire started."

He ran to the small shanty. With the wood and matches always found in such cabins, he soon had a fire blazing. Then he returned and helped Joe back to the shelter. Joe's hands, feet, and face were in bad condition.

"We'll have to get you back to the post as fast as possible and tend to those feet and hands. Warm up while I hitch up the dogs."

Swiftly Bobby fastened Snooky to the sled as lead dog. The other dogs snarled and tangled their traces. But Bobby gave the fighters a lash with the driver's whip. That stopped all the commotion, and the dogs fell into their places.

"I . . . can't walk," said Joe, gritting his teeth against the pain as feeling flowed back into his frozen feet. "Help me get on top."

"I'll put this moosehide blanket around you," said Bobby. "Keep your face covered." Bobby helped Joe get on the loaded sled and covered him snugly.

"Now, Snooky," commanded Bobby, "march! Let's go!"

Snooky started off briskly. Bobby ran behind the sled, following the flying dog team.

Bobby's father spent no time asking Joe what happened. Neither did he scold Bobby for leaving the cabin without telling anyone. He did not even marvel at Snooky's dog-sense. The other dog trains had arrived. After making sure Joe was being cared for, Father got back to the business of unpacking the fur-packs and examining and counting the pelts before the plane came in the next day.

Bobby felt a little hurt that nobody paid any attention to him and Snooky. After all, they had saved Joe's life. All his father said was, "See to the dogs, Bobby."

The next day, after the airplane had taken off with the furs, Bobby's father said, "Son, I'm buying another pair of dogs for the regular routes. I'm retiring Fancy and her partner for good."

"What about Snooky?" asked Bobby. "I thought you were giving Snooky his mother's place."

"No," said his father slowly, "I'm putting Snooky on that Crooked River trail. We'll pick up the pelts there once a week."

Bobby said nothing. Only three days ago he would have had plenty to say. He would have begged his father to let him take over the Crooked River trail.

Oh, yes, he knew the Crooked River trail. He knew how to handle Snooky and the dog team. But now he also knew there were things he could not handle—and one of them was the weather. Now he didn't *want* to run the trail alone—not even with Snooky.

Then his father continued, "I figured you could begin going along with the driver. You know the trail pretty well. He will probably let you drive Snooky part of the time. A good dog-team driver should start young. It will be a good chance for you to get some experience and yet not be out on the trail alone."

# Chums

He sits and begs, he gives a paw,
   He is, as you can see,
The finest dog you ever saw,
   And he belongs to me.

He follows everywhere I go
   And even when I swim.
I laugh because he thinks, you know,
   That I belong to him.

But still no matter what we do
   We never have a fuss;
And so I guess it must be true
   That *we* belong to *us*.

    –Arthur Guiterman

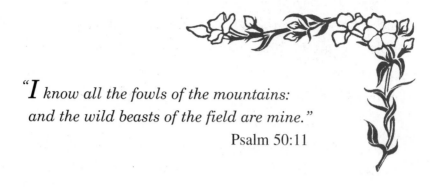

*"I know all the fowls of the mountains:
and the wild beasts of the field are mine."*

Psalm 50:11

# A Foxy Father

Through the melting snow on the high hill that sloped
down to the river came a pair of foxes. Domino's black fur,
tipped with white, gave him a silver look. A black mark
across his eyes made him handsome indeed. Snowyruff, a
dainty little lady fox, ran by his side. She wore a red coat
and an **elegant** ruffle of white. They had met one day in the
woods, and chosen each other as mates and friends for life,
as foxes always do. Now they searched through the woods
for a place to build their den.

Snowyruff looked about the sheltered hillside, nosed the
ground, then began to dig. That meant, "We'll set up house-
keeping here."

She did not know that she had chosen the same sunny

slope on which Domino himself had lived as a tiny pup. She only saw it as a fine place for a family of foxes to make their home. Sheltered from the wind and warmed by the sun, the entrance to the den lay within a pine **thicket.**

The snow and thick leaves had kept the earth soft enough for Snowyruff to dig. Domino sat openly on the hill keeping watch for a long time. Then he took her place and dug while Snowyruff kept watch. So, working together, they **excavated** their home—a cozy den, impossible to see even a dozen feet away. As spring advanced, the growing grass hid it even better. The pair took great care not to be seen near the den.

At last one day Snowyruff let Domino know that he must leave her alone, so he went no more to the den. In his absence five little blind foxes were born! When Snowyruff left them to slip down to the river for a cool drink of water, Domino lay there on the bank watching. She told him in plain fox language, "You must not come home yet." He crouched with his head flat on the leaves as she hurried back to the den, but he did not attempt to follow.

Those days, she ate some of the food they had stored in the dry sand of the den's side chamber. Two days later she found a dead rabbit near the entrance to the den. Domino had stolen down and left it for her and their babies. Every day after that she found at the doorway or hidden in the grass nearby food he had managed to **capture.**

Nine days after birth, the pups' eyes opened. They whimpered less, for now they could see their mother.

84

They could scramble to the entrance and look out. They could see to play with each other.

Domino now joined his family. He guarded them with the greatest care, as devoted to them as Mother Snowyruff herself. Before long, the parents brought their toddlers out into the sunlight in front of the den. There they tumbled and romped and wrestled with each other. Sometimes they snapped at flies or chased bumblebees. Sometimes they made a fine game of catching Mother's tail, or tussled over a duck's wing.

The days passed and the young foxes grew stronger. Domino and Snowyruff began teaching them to hunt for themselves. They brought live game home each day. Sometimes they brought a frog or a fat field mouse, then turned it loose for the youngsters to recapture.

One day Domino called, *Chur-chur-chur.* When the pups came tumbling over one another, he dropped a live muskrat among them. They pounced on it, but the muskrat fought desperately. Even though it seemed that he would win, the father and mother only watched. Their children must learn to capture and kill their own food. So they waited until together the five pups conquered the muskrat.

The happy growing days went by. The cubs had not yet learned the meaning of fear. Their existence in the hidden hillside den was one of peace and safety.

One day when Domino returned home with food, five little black noses and ten little beady eyes, set in woolly heads, filled the entrance to the den. Suddenly a hound

**bayed** nearby. Domino leaped on a stump to listen. The hound bayed again, closer this time. His sharp nose had picked up Domino's scent and he was coming on excitedly.

Snowyruff warned the little ones and herded them out of sight. Domino **loped** out to meet his enemy. He showed himself boldly, and barked defiance at the big hound. Then he leaped away, leading the dog away from the den.

Domino fled ahead of the pursuing hound. He plunged through thickets trying to throw the dog off his trail. He doubled, crossed, backtracked, and leaped across the stream, but the old hound knew every trick. No matter what the fox did, the baying hound loped heavily after him, determined to capture the fleeing fox.

At last Domino led his enemy along a narrow ledge that ran upward along a cliff overhanging the river.

Up and up they went; Domino trotted slower and slower. Now the hound could see him just ahead and put on a burst of speed. At last Domino reached the top of the cliff. His silver coat gleamed against the sky. At the very edge he turned to face his enemy.

The hound plunged forward, leaping at the fox. Domino sprang lightly aside, and the hound plunged headlong over the rugged cliff. He splashed into the icy flood below. Battered and bleeding he struggled to the shore and limped home, whining with pain.

Domino turned back and trotted tiredly home. There, five little black noses and ten little beady eyes, set in five little woolly heads, waited for their father. There, his dainty little wife with the elegant white ruffle welcomed him home.

The hound never came back. Domino and Snowyruff cared for their family until the little foxes grew large enough to leave the home den and make homes for themselves.

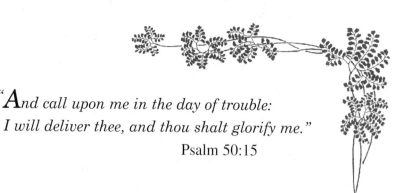

*"And call upon me in the day of trouble:
I will deliver thee, and thou shalt glorify me."*
Psalm 50:15

# If It Hadn't Been for Buster

A whimpering little bear cub waddled up to me one rainy day. He had come out of the trees with soaked fur and a mud-covered **muzzle.** My first thought—*where was his mother?* Every **article** I ever read, every man I had ever talked with about bears warned me to steer clear of a bear with a cub. But I gathered the lonely little thing into my arms. Keeping a sharp lookout for his mother, I carried him to my cabin. There I fastened the door and set the cub down in front of the cheerful fireplace. He curled up at once and went to sleep.

Darkness fell as I cooked supper. While I ate, the cub woke up and began to walk around. He **nuzzled** every article he could reach in the entire cabin. "I'm hungry," he told me in plain bear language.

I had been eating pancakes, bacon, and coffee. I offered him all three, but he would not eat them.

I knew bears like fish, so I opened a can of sardines. He gobbled them down in six wags of his little tail. A bear that young needed milk, so I gave him canned milk thinned with water. It took an hour's time and two cans of milk before he learned to lie on his back and slurp from a long-necked bottle. After he had learned this trick, whenever he got hungry, he would hunt up the bottle. Then he would lie on his back and suck at it until I saw him and filled it with milk.

That night when I went to bed, I left the cub asleep before the fire. During the night I dreamed someone put me in a cider press and squeezed me so that I could not breathe. I woke up to find the cub on my chest. He nuzzled me **affectionately.** I knew the little fellow felt lonely without his mother.

The next day I fed him more sardines and a full bottle of milk. He seemed content to stay around the cabin, and followed me in and out like a puppy.

About nine o'clock the next evening I heard a grunting, snuffling noise outside. The cub heard it too, and scampered, whining, to the door. A thrill of fear shot through me. The mother bear had trailed her baby to my cabin. Of course, she wanted her baby. If I let him out perhaps she would give me no trouble.

By this time she was making a great **commotion,** growling and scratching at the door. She meant to have her cub.

With my gun in one hand, I carefully opened the door a few inches with my foot braced against it. Instantly the cub had his muzzle in the opening and squeezed out to join his mother. That ended the commotion.

I watched the two through the window as the mother nuzzled her cub in the moonlight. Satisfied, she waddled down the path that led to the deep woods and the creek. The cub trotted after her for a few yards, then stopped. The old one turned and cuffed it. He went along all right for a few more yards before stopping again. After several more cuffs, the two trotted into the underbrush.

I felt lonely that night. While a bear is not a perfect pet, it is company.

A few days after the cub had gone off with its mother, I heard a whining at the door. Cautiously I opened it, and in walked my cub.

The long-necked bottle lay near the fireplace. Without looking at me, the little bear took the bottle, turned on his back and began sucking. I hastily filled the bottle. After finishing that, he ate a can of sardines, then went to sleep before the fire.

I was glad the cub had returned, but I couldn't forget the mother bear. I knew she would come again. I had to think of some way to prevent her coming into the cabin when I let out the cub.

Finally I bored a two-inch hole in the floor just inside the door. Into this I fitted a sturdy peg. The peg acted as a doorstop, allowing the door to open only about six or seven inches. The cub could squeeze through the opening, but the mother could get not so much as her muzzle in. I felt safe after that.

That night I did not wait for the cub to climb into my bed. I tucked him in with me. He nuzzled my neck, then cuddled up to me affectionately.

I never saw the mother again, but all that spring the little bear made visits to my cabin. I named him Buster. When he first came to me, he stood no higher than a poodle dog. But within two months he could hardly get through the door when the peg was in place.

Buster grew so large that sometimes I wondered if he might not turn on me someday. My neighbors advised me to kill him before he attacked me, but that I could not do.

During the summer I saw little of him, and wondered if he had forgotten me and left the area. But one noon I returned to the cabin from a fishing trip down the creek. I was carrying my catch of four big trout, when I heard a commotion in the berry bushes. Then Buster appeared, huge and friendly. He nuzzled me affectionately as usual, and with a watering mouth followed me up to the cabin. With a twitching muzzle he watched me clean the fish. I threw him the pieces of waste, but he did not try to get more than I threw to him. After I had cooked all I could eat, he finished the rest. Now I knew Buster had not forgotten me.

In late summer when the crops were in, I began clearing a patch of ground about a hundred yards from the cabin. I would chop down a tree, cut off its branches and saw the trunk into three-foot lengths. I piled the brush to the side and hauled the wood to the cabin. In this way I cleared the land and cut my winter firewood at the same time.

One morning in the early fall, I began on another tree, putting the cut on the south side so it would fall that way. But a sudden gust of wind caught the top and swung it toward the east. It fell against a slim standing tree and hung there. Now I had to cut that tree to fell the first one. I had no more than begun when either the jarring blows of the axe or the wind loosened the first tree. Without warning, it crashed. It slammed me to the ground, pinning me there. I heard my right leg snap as a limb caught it. Another limb held my left arm down. Numerous branches on the lower side held the trunk somewhat off the ground or I would have been smashed like a beetle. I heard myself cry, "God, help me," before I passed out from the terrible pain in my chest.

Late in the afternoon I came to with a raging thirst. I felt feverish and could not distinguish the pain in my leg from the agony in my chest. Then I fainted again. All that night I dreamed off and on of water and would wake up almost wild for a drink. Finally I lost all track of time.

The morning sun, hot and terrible, woke me the next day. My head cleared enough so that I could take stock of my situation. A mile of wild country lay between me and the road. No one from that direction would hear me if I called. Neighbors did not visit me very often—sometimes for a week or so. One fact stared me in the face. Unless God sent some-one, I would die of thirst if my wounds did not kill me first.

Then I heard a dog barking. My hopes rose. Perhaps a man would be with the dog. At that moment a black muzzle poked through the leaves and a huge form lumbered from the bushes. Buster! The bear pushed through the branches of the tree and nuzzled my face. Then he backed out and sat there whining as if he knew something was wrong. Cocking his head to one side he looked at me with a puzzled expression.

Then a dog broke through the underbrush, his nose to the ground, following Buster's trail. The bear raised up on his haunches ready for battle. The dog stopped.

Suddenly I heard voices and I shouted in weak desperation.

A man's voice cried, "There's someone there!"

"Here. Under the tree," I called. "Hold your dog. The bear's my pet."

A minute later my neighbors stepped into sight, One of them called to the dog. Buster lumbered away through the trees and disappeared.

The men said they had been trailing a deer when the dog ran across the bear's tracks and took up the new trail.

My friends soon set me free and took me to my cabin. One of them stayed with me while the other went home to get a horse and ride for the doctor.

Within 24 hours I found myself in the hospital wrapped in bandages, with my leg in a cast.

My neighbors said they would take care of things at my cabin. They promised to set out a can or two of sardines for

my bear. They agreed that I would have died there in the woods if it hadn't been for Buster. But, of course, I knew it was God who had sent my pet that day.

*All of the animals you have read about so far can be found in the book that this poem describes. Have you ever read this book? Did you ever look up into the sky and think you were looking at a book's cover?*

# The Book of Nature

There are many good books, my child,
    And a very good book for you
Is the book that is hid in the greenwood wild,
    All bound in a cover of blue.

'Tis the book of the birds and the bees,
    Of the flowers, and the fish in the brook;
You may learn how to read if you go to the
        trees
    And open your eyes and look.

                   –Charter Keeler

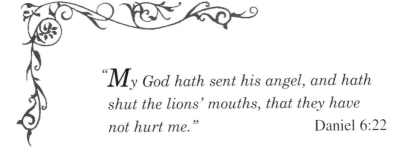

*"**M**y God hath sent his angel, and hath shut the lions' mouths, that they have not hurt me."*        Daniel 6:22

# In Spite of Lions

*Words in brackets [ ] after several harder words tell you what the harder words mean. When you come to a word in brackets, just read it in place of the word after which it comes.*

¹⁰ Now when Daniel knew that the writing was signed, he went into his house; and his windows being open in his **chamber** toward Jerusalem, he kneeled upon his knees three times a day, and prayed, and gave thanks before his God, as he did aforetime [before].

¹¹ Then these men **assembled,** and found Daniel praying and making **supplication** before his God.

¹² Then they came near, and spake before the king concerning the king's **decree;** Hast thou not signed a decree, that every man that shall ask a **petition** of any God or man

98

within thirty days, save of thee, O king, shall be cast into the den of lions?

The king answered and said, The thing is true, according to the law of the Medes[1] and Persians[2], which altereth [changes] not.

[13] Then answered they and said before the king, That Daniel, which is of the children of the captivity of Judah, regardeth not thee, O king, nor the decree that thou hast signed, but maketh his petition three times a day.

[14] Then the king, when he heard these words, was sore displeased with himself, and set his heart on Daniel to deliver him: and he laboured till the going down of the sun to deliver him.

[15] Then these men assembled unto the king, and said unto the king, Know, O king, that the law of the Medes and Persians is, That no decree nor statute [law] which the king establisheth [makes] may be changed.

---

[1]Medes – mēdz
[2]Persians – pər′ zhənz

¹⁶ Then the king commanded, and they brought Daniel, and cast him into the den of lions.

Now the king spake and said unto Daniel, Thy God whom thou servest continually, he will deliver thee.

¹⁷ And a stone was brought, and laid upon the mouth of the den; and the king sealed it with his own signet, and with the signet of his lords; that the purpose might not be changed concerning Daniel.

¹⁸ Then the king went to his palace, and passed the night fasting: neither were instruments of musick brought before him: and his sleep went from him.

¹⁹ Then the king arose very early in the morning, and went in haste unto the den of lions. ²⁰ And when he came to the den, he cried with a lamentable [sad] voice unto Daniel: and the king spake and said to Daniel, O Daniel, servant of

the living God, is thy God, whom thou servest continually, able to deliver thee from the lions?

21 Then said Daniel unto the king, O king, live for ever. 22 My God hath sent his angel, and hath shut the lions' mouths, that they have not hurt me: forasmuch as before him innocency was found in me; and also before thee, O king, have I done no hurt.

23 Then was the king exceeding glad for him, and commanded that they should take Daniel up out of the den. So Daniel was taken up out of the den, and no manner of hurt was found upon him, because he believed in his God.

–Daniel 6

*Some wild animals are dangerous to people and to other animals. Daniel's enemies expected the lions in the den to kill him, but God was in control, so they could not kill him. Notice how this verse pictures all things under God's control living together peaceably.*

# The Peaceable Kingdom

The wolf also shall dwell with the lamb,
and the leopard shall lie down with the kid;
and the calf and the young lion and the
    fatling together;
and a little child shall lead them.

–Isaiah 11:6

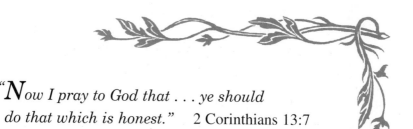

*"**N**ow I pray to God that . . . ye should
do that which is honest."*   2 Corinthians 13:7

# No Difference at All

Rachel said to herself, "Well, it won't do any harm to ask him."

She turned her back on Mr. Hilton's private **wharf** at Eel Pond. Tied up there floated the skiffs that Mr. Hilton made during the wintertime and rented to summer visitors. Ahead of Rachel was the door opening into Mr. Hilton's carpenter shop. After a short **pause**, she walked into the shop with an air of determination. A tall man in overalls was busy at the workbench.

"Mr. Hilton!"

The man looked up. "Eh?"

"Mr. Hilton, how much are you renting skiffs for?"

"Ten dollars for the season," Mr. Hilton replied, "with the oars thrown in." Then after a short **mental** pause, he added, "Two pairs if you want them. Then your little sister can row with you. Do you want to pick out one of the skiffs now? I'll go down to the wharf with you."

"No—not now," Rachel told him. "I have to go help Father now. I'll—I'll be back."

She left and walked quickly in the direction of the **laboratory**, wondering how she could make some money faster than working for her father. Just now she owned exactly seven dollars and eighty-five cents. It was more money than she usually had, but still not enough.

Rachel's father was one of the **scientists** working at the Elsworth Shore Laboratory. On her twelfth birthday, he had suggested a wonderful plan. She would assist him in the laboratory at twenty cents an hour. By the end of the summer she would have made a nice amount of money.

The trouble was that she did not want to wait until August for her boat. She wanted it right now, to use the rest of the summer.

In the square entrance hall of the laboratory, Rachel found a group of lively children, including her little sister Rosalind. Rozzy, as they called her, did not see her big sister come in. The whole group clustered around Edgar. Rachel knew what held their interest.

In the very center of the hall, on a

skiff – a small rowboat with a flat bottom

heavy support, stood a statue of a large elephant. It was of shining brass, a gift to the laboratory from an elderly rich man. This elephant, named Edgar, had a small open mouth under his upward-curving trunk. This open mouth was now a part of a delightful little game. A scientist going by, with no one else in the hall to see him, would slip his hand into his pocket and take out a penny. Then quickly he would place the penny in Edgar's mouth. And the first child to find it there could keep it.

This time there was no penny, and the children ran out laughing. Rachel smiled to herself as she climbed the stairs, remembering when she had been a small girl and had now and then found a gift from Edgar. But now she was not a child. Years ago she had stopped taking the pennies, even when she had seen them first.

By the time Rachel had reached the first landing, she heard someone coming down the long hallway below. She paused, looking back. The newcomer was an elderly man whose face Rachel recognized at once. He was looking out of the door to where the children were running gaily down to the **pier**. A pleased smile crossed his face as he turned toward the brass elephant. Rachel understood the smile, for this was the man who had brought the statue from Africa and presented it to the laboratory at Elsworth Shore.

Quickly he took a coin from his pocket and placed it in Edgar's mouth. Then he went back the way he had come.

Rachel leaned over the stairway railing with widening eyes. Could it be—it couldn't—but it was! A whole silver dollar, perfectly huge! What couldn't you do with a whole dollar!

Rachel raced down the stairs. She took the fat coin and held it in her fist while she did some rapid mental arithmetic. That dollar added to her $7.85 would make $8.85. Daddy would pay her $1.20 for six hours of washing laboratory dishes. She would put 15¢ of that in the offering plate on Sunday. That would leave $1.05 to add to her $8.85, making a total of $9.90. And Rozzy had offered to lend her 10¢ of her weekly allowance. That would complete the sum needed for the rent of the skiff.

"Whee!" said Rachel softly. She quickly looked up and down the hall, but saw no one. Then she trotted lightly up the steps.

Her father stood working at the long table under the windows of his laboratory room.

She set a pan of water over the gas flame to heat and looked out of the windows at the blue salt water of Eel Pond and the skiffs tied up to the pier there. When the dishwater boiled, she began absentmindedly to wash the dishes that her father had left for her. He seemed to have eyes in the back of his head, for he said, without turning round, "Better do that batch over again, Rachel. You didn't scald the rack."

He was right. She hadn't. Her mental travels had taken her far away. Rachel had to heat more water. With laboratory dishes, she knew very well, it was of no use to be *almost* clean. A few germs picked up from a drying rack that hadn't been scalded might be enough to ruin a whole science experiment. Everything had to be strictly and completely clean.

*That is the difference,* Rachel thought, *between science and—well, ordinary life. In ordinary life, if you are strictly and completely honest, you never get anywhere. You would never get anything you want—for example, a skiff at the beginning of summer.*

Like this dollar! It really did not belong to Rachel at all. The man meant it for the small children. But small children didn't care about money. They didn't know how to use it. A penny gave a child just as much pleasure as a dollar. Look at Rozzy. Ten cents was probably all the money she had in the world, and yet she had offered to lend it all.

When Rachel had finished her work, she said good-bye to her father and went slowly downstairs. The dollar felt strangely heavy in her pocket. She kept her hand over it, and when she got to the landing, she paused and looked down.

Two children were standing beside Edgar in the wide hall below. One of them was Rozzy, the other a small boy about the same age. Rozzy's busy fingers were exploring the statue's mouth.

"Perfectly empty," she reported.

"Well, you have a dime tied up in your handkerchief," said the boy. "You could buy two ice-cream cones with that."

"Yes, I could," agreed Rozzy, "but I promised that dime to Rachel, so I can't spend it for anything."

"Not even for that boat in Mrs. Thompson's window?" teased the boy.

"Not even for that boat—even if it cost only a dime instead of a dollar," declared Rozzy firmly.

"Oh, all right," said her companion, as the two went outside.

"That's just what I was saying," Rachel murmured, mentally continuing an argument with someone. "Rozzy's not getting anywhere by being so honest. She can't even buy an ice-cream cone for herself and her friend, let alone that boat she wants so badly."

Rachel came on down the stairs, slow step after slow step. At the brass figure she stopped. Until this minute she had very conveniently forgotten how badly Rozzy wanted the beautiful toy ship in the shop window. With a whole dollar she could buy it.

With a sigh, Rachel took out the silver dollar and laid it in Edgar's mouth. It was hard to part with it, but now it was the only thing to do.

She went out into the clear sunshine and down toward the pier, and there was Rozzy.

"Listen, Rozzy," Rachel said, putting temptation behind her firmly, "run up and see if Dad doesn't want some letters mailed."

Rozzy sped across the laboratory lawn at once. She couldn't visit her father's laboratory except on business, and she loved going there whenever she had the chance.

Rachel strolled slowly down the street. In front of Mrs. Thompson's shop window she paused. There sat the toy boat for which Rozzy had been longing. She walked on and had almost reached Mr. Hilton's carpenter shop when she heard running feet and felt a hand grab her by the elbow.

"Oh, Rachel," Rozzy gasped, "a whole dollar!" She held it up in front of Rachel's nose. "From Edgar," she explained breathlessly. "He never did have so much money before, and it's all mine. Nobody else was there."

"Well," said Rachel, "how wonderful! What are you going to do with it? Buy Mrs. Thompson's boat?"

To her surprise Rozzy did not answer with the glad "Yes" she had expected. She stopped Rachel with a tug on her arm squarely in front of the carpenter shop.

"Please, Rachel," she begged, "can't I give you this dollar and my dime, and have a share in your skiff this summer?"

Mr. Hilton, looking up from his workbench, saw Rachel lift Rozzy in her arms and hug her very tightly. He waited until she had set her sister back on the walk, and then he went to the open shop door.

"Of course," Mr. Hilton began, just as if they were simply going on with an earlier conversation, "of course, if you wanted to, you could pay something down now on a skiff and the rest of the rent later, at your convenience."

Rachel and Rozzy looked up at him with big eyes.

"I have known your father these fifteen years, and he has never lost a pair of oars for me yet."

"But it isn't Father who is renting it," explained Rachel. "This year I am renting it—or at least, Rozzy and I are."

Rozzy stepped closer to Rachel's side.

"I expect honest dealing runs in the family," Mr. Hilton said with a twinkle in his eye.

*Maybe it does,* Rachel thought with a happy leap of the

heart. *I didn't keep the dollar.* Aloud she asked, "Would eight dollars and ninety-five cents be enough for now?"

"You bring it to me and choose your boat."

"I can give you a dollar and ten cents now," Rozzy offered.

"Down payment," Rachel said, remembering the proper phrase.

"In that case we might save time by picking out the boat now," Mr. Hilton answered.

Rozzy ran ahead toward Mr. Hilton's private wharf shouting, "Let's name it *The R and R.*"

The carpenter followed. But Rachel stood still, a surprised look on her face. "I was wrong about ordinary life," she said to herself. "If I had kept the dollar to rent the skiff, I'd have been miserable every time I used it—at least until I confessed. Rozzy would be sorry her big sister had done such a thing, and Mr. Hilton would never trust me again. *That's* where that dishonest dollar would have gotten me!

"Yes, I was wrong," she murmured, going on. "Being strictly and completely honest is the *only* way to get anywhere in life. It's just like being strictly and completely clean in a science experiment. There is no difference at all."

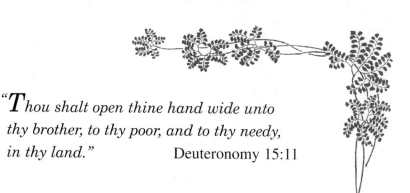

*"Thou shalt open thine hand wide unto thy brother, to thy poor, and to thy needy, in thy land."* Deuteronomy 15:11

# What's a Fish Between Friends?

The sun's first rays **glistened** on the top of the giant **sycamore** when Rick stopped at the small cottage where his best friend lived. Rick carried a tin bucket of lunch, filled with plenty of goodies for both boys. Rick's mom always packed enough for Jess when the boys went on an **excursion** together. "It's just as easy to put in enough for two as for one, while I'm at it," she had once said. Rick had never thought about why she did it. He put his fingers to his mouth and gave his usual shrill whistle for his friend.

Jess appeared immediately, pausing only to pick up his fishing pole leaning against the house.

Then the door opened again and Jess's little sister ran out. "Here, Jess, you forgot your breakfast. Mother said you

shouldn't go without breakfast," she said, handing the boy a biscuit.

"Thanks, Betsy," said Jess. He took the biscuit and **devoured** it in three quick bites as they walked along.

*Breakfast? One biscuit?* thought Rick. *That's no breakfast. Is that all they had? Maybe that's why Mother packs lunch for Jess too.* But then Rick's mind went back to fishing.

It was one of those perfect mornings for an excursion. Dew glistened from every grass blade under their eager feet. Two bobwhites whistled to each other across the hay field. Leaves **quivered** in a teasing little breeze that bore the sweet June fragrance of locust blossoms.

At the old covered bridge, conversation ceased. Sliding down the bank, they crept beneath the damp timbers and pushed on through the bushes bordering the creek.

At last they reached the dead sycamore that had fallen across the dark waters of their favorite fishing hole. A lizard lay there blinking his yellow eyes at them, then scuttled to the underside of the log. A huge bullfrog leaped off a rock at their feet and splashed headfirst into the water.

Easing out onto the center of the log, the boys opened the can of worms and baited their hooks "just so." They cast in their lines with the greatest care and settled down, without a word, to wait for a bite. It may have been half an hour before Rick's line quivered and a circle of ripples spread out around it.

Rick waited. He did not even breathe. Then, with a

strong tug, the cork bobbed under.

"Jerk him out, Rick! Jerk him out!" shouted Jess.

Rick jerked hard. The pole bent in a thrilling way. Rick stood up and lifted. The line cleared the water, and a beautiful speckled trout **flounced** and glistened in the sunlight.

Together the boys got the fish to the bank.

"Rick, isn't he a wonder?" cried Jess.

"Isn't he?" shouted Rick. "Now isn't he? My family always laughs when I go fishing because I never catch anything. They'll stop their laughing when they see this fellow."

The boys strung the trout and tied one end of the cord to a root of the old sycamore. The fish swam back and forth in the clear water, while the delighted boys watched it. Then Rick baited his hook again.

"I hope you get the next one, Jess," said Rick, as they settled on the log again.

But Jess caught no fish. Once or twice his line quivered, but it was only a minnow stealing the bait. The boys waited, whispering quietly until the sun stood exactly overhead. Then they ate their lunch. Rick noticed for the first time how quickly Jess devoured his share of what Mother had sent. After putting fresh bait on their lines, they dropped them in and waited some more. But in vain. No more bites—not even a nibble. The shadows grew long, and the boys knew they had to give up.

"Well, we should go, I suppose," said Rick.

"Yes," agreed Jess. "Not much hope of catching any more."

They wound their lines and pulled up the trout. Shouldering their poles, they retraced their steps through the bushes, under the bridge and up the bank.

Rick's heart felt lighter than a balloon. How he would surprise the family when he came home with his fish! They would never dare make fun of his fishing trips again. He would show them a fish that was a fish!

The boys saw Betsy swinging on the gate when they neared the little cottage. "Jess, did you get any fish?" she called out.

"Not today," replied Jess. "But Rick got one, and it is a beauty. Show it to her, Rick."

As they came closer Rick held up the trout. Betsy devoured it with her eyes.

Suddenly Rick realized that the little girl wanted that fish, really wanted it. But she only called gaily, "Rick, you are a sure-enough fisherman now!"

"Yes, and I know who I am going to give my fish to," said Rick, and he handed the stringer to Betsy.

"No," cried the astonished child. "I can't take it. You caught it!" But her voice quivered with eagerness.

Rick only laughed and left the fish in her hands. "See you, Jess," he said, and started up the hill toward home.

Supper would be waiting on the back porch. There would be chicken and green peas and asparagus, he knew. And, likely as not, cherry tarts. He had helped pick the cherries the day before. At his home they didn't need fish for food. But down at the tiny house where Jess and Betsy

116

and their mother lived, that fish might be about all they had to eat that evening. Perhaps there would not be very much of a supper without it. And if his family did not believe him when he told them what a big fish he had caught—well, that did not matter so much anyway!

# The Fisherman

The fisherman goes out at dawn
  When everyone's abed,
And from the bottom of the sea
  Draws up his daily bread.

His life is strange; half on the shore
  And half upon the sea—
Not quite a fish, and yet not quite
  The same as you and me.

He knows so much of boats and tides,
  Of winds and clouds and sky!
But when I tell of city things,
  He sniffs and shuts one eye!

—Abbie Farwell Brown

118

# A Boy's Song

Where the pools are bright and deep,
Where the gray trout lies asleep,
Up the river and over the lea,
That's the way for Billy and me.

Where the blackbird sings the latest,
Where the hawthorn blooms the sweetest,
Where the nestlings chirp and flee,
That's the way for Billy and me.

Where the mowers mow the cleanest,
Where the hay lies thick and greenest,
There to track the homeward bee,
That's the way for Billy and me.

Where the hazel bank is steepest,
Where the shadow falls the deepest,
Where the clustering nuts fall free,
That's the way for Billy and me.

— James Hogg

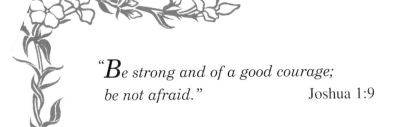

"*Be strong and of a good courage; be not afraid.*"    Joshua 1:9

# No More Molasses Cookies

*Inger Johanne was a little girl who lived in Norway. Her name is pronounced like this: In'ger Yō hän´ə. She was very lively and got into a good deal of mischief without really meaning to do so. She has written some stories about herself, and this is one of them.*

Everyone in our town says that Mrs. Simonsen's molasses cookies are the best in the world—they are so thick and soft and tasty. Mrs. Simonsen doesn't make them herself. Heinrich Schulze, the head baker, does that. But she stands behind the counter in her shop and sells them every day.

Ever since Mrs. Simonsen's husband died, Heinrich Schulze has been the head baker.

Although I have been **acquainted** with Mrs. Simonsen for a long time, there is no use in going into her shop without money. Whenever I do have money, though, I go there and buy molasses cookies.

If I have no money, I go in the back way through the gate and beg some cookies from Heinrich Schulze. In fact, I go the back way most often.

I can usually find him in the yard there, hurrying to and fro between the shop and the bakery. Often the molasses cookie dough hangs over his shoulder like a long sausage.

Schulze says that good molasses cookie dough should be so tough that it will hang over one's shoulder without breaking. Some people think it is disgusting for him to carry the dough that way, but I don't think it is disgusting at all. I even pinch off a **morsel** and eat it raw, right from his shoulder, very often.

I am much better acquainted with Schulze. He and I are great friends, let me tell you. He is German, and is rather old and small. He has black eyes and is very wide-awake, and quick.

I know exactly the days when he bakes molasses cookies. On those days I hang around the bake-house door and beg. I say, "Please give me a little dough, Schulze, just a little morsel, Schulze." He always gives me some, usually a good-sized morsel.

One Wednesday afternoon, Schulze, with the dough over his shoulder, came swinging out of the shop into the back yard. I sat there on an empty flour barrel, waiting for him. I was holding a tiny china doll in my hand.

Schulze was in a grand good **humor** that day. He stopped beside the barrel.

"Young lady, it may happen that I shall someday be master of this bakery here. Then Heinrich Schulze will be the boss. He can snap his fingers at the whole wide world," said Schulze. He had the dough over his shoulder and was flouncing around in front of me and snapping his fingers in the air as he spoke.

I don't know what made me think of it. While Schulze pranced around swinging his arms and snapping his fingers right and left, I stuck that little china doll right into the dough. Schulze didn't notice what I was doing. The dough closed over the place where I had poked in the doll, and a moment later, Schulze flounced on into the bake-house.

"What fun it will be when he finds the doll in the dough!" I said to myself. "In a minute he will come storming out here pretending to be angry. Then we will have a good laugh over it." So I sat still on the barrel and waited. But Schulze did not come out.

*Oh, well,* I thought, *he just wants to* **deceive** *me by pretending he hasn't found the doll.*

I stole over to the bake-house door. The molasses cookies stood in the pans, ready to go into the oven that very minute.

Schulze never likes to have anyone come into the bake-house and interrupt his baking, so I dared not go farther than the door. He looked up and smiled at me, so I knew the doll had not put him in a bad humor. But not a word

did he say about it. He was surely trying to deceive me into thinking he had not found it.

Suddenly I remembered that I had not done my homework. Lessons always seem to interrupt my fun. I started on a run for home. My joke would have to wait.

That whole evening I laughed to myself every time I thought of the doll in the cookie dough. I would get the little thing back from Schulze in the morning on my way to school.

But when I looked in the bakery door the next day, he did not say a word about it. He didn't act as if he knew about any joke. Maybe he wasn't trying to deceive me after all.

Maybe he had not found the doll! Suppose it was baked in a cookie and sold, and someone should bite on it and break a tooth. Suppose someone should cut his mouth on the broken doll. Suppose someone should swallow it and become very ill.

These dreadful thoughts swarmed into my mind as I went on to school. I grew frightened. I didn't dare say a word to anyone about it, though. Mrs. Simonsen and Schulze would be furious if they knew what I had done. Perhaps someone in the town was sick in bed today. Maybe they would need an operation to get the doll out of their stomach, all because of that molasses cookie with my little china doll in it!

Oh, how I suffered that day! After school I asked Father for some money and spent it all on molasses cookies. I hoped the little doll might be in one of those I bought. But I grew more desperate with each one I ate. I ate so many molasses cookies, I got perfectly sick of them. I ate them with despair in my heart and ended up with no doll.

At last I went and stood beside the steps of Mrs. Simonsen's shop and stared at everyone who came out who had bought molasses cookies.

*Perhaps it is you who will get the doll in your stomach—or perhaps it is you,* I kept thinking. However, I could not bring myself to warn any of them even though I worried so fiercely. I simply did not have the courage.

When children bought the cookies, however, I took their cookies—whether they liked it or not—and squeezed them to find out whether the doll was inside. No, I did not find it.

At last I was so anxious that I felt truly sick. Several times I was on the point of going in and telling Mrs. Simonsen. That was just too difficult, though. I simply did not have the courage to do it. At the same time, I knew I would have to do it sometime.

At last I had to go home to supper. That night I dreamed of the doll in the cookies.

The next afternoon, when I came from school, I sat down again on the steps of the bakery. I hoped, yet dreaded, to hear some word about my china doll. Mrs. Simonsen stood in the doorway, sunning herself. She was in a good humor for a change. I tried to think what words I could use to tell her what I had done.

"It is warm and pleasant these days," she said.

Yes, I, too, thought it was very warm. Indeed, I broke into a sweat whenever I thought of the molasses cookies with the doll in it.

"Why, if that isn't the Collector of the Port himself coming," Mrs. Simonsen interrupted my nervous thoughts. "He is coming to my shop, I declare! Go away from the steps, child. I don't want him to see a dirty little girl hanging around my bake shop."

I was not acquainted with the Collector of the Port. But I knew he was a very important person. So, of course, Mrs. Simonsen felt pleased to have him come to her shop.

Yes, there he came, with his keen face, his bent back, and his cap with a broad gold braid on it. He stopped beside the steps, stuck his cane between the paving-stones and looked up at Mrs. Simonsen in the doorway.

"Is this Mrs. Simonsen who sells molasses cookies?"

Mrs. Simonsen curtsied. "Yes, your honor," she answered, politely, holding open the door.

The old wooden steps creaked under the Collector's heavy step. Now he was in the shop. I peeped in at the door. I could tell he was in a bad humor.

"May I then ask you, my good woman," said the Collector, "what you call this?"

He searched in one vest pocket, searched a long time—searched in the other vest pocket. Then, between his crooked thumb and big pointer finger, he held high in the air my little china doll!

The instant I saw it, I was awfully glad, for now I knew

no one had swallowed it, and that it was not lying in any-one's stomach causing pain, if not death.

"What do you call this?" repeated the Collector. He stared at Mrs. Simonsen from under his terrifying, bushy eyebrows.

There was a blank look in Mrs. Simonsen's sky-blue eyes as she looked from the doll to the Collector and from the Collector to the doll. He had to ask her three times before she answered.

"That—that is a—a doll," said Mrs. Simonsen at last.

"Yes, perfectly true—a doll. Then may I ask what a doll was doing in my molasses cookie? Why was it there, I ask you? Tell me that."

"In your molasses cookie?" exclaimed Mrs. Simonsen in the utmost astonishment. It seemed, however, as if she were a little braver now that the talk came to molasses cookies.

"Yes, right in the molasses cookie," snapped the Collector. "I sat drinking my coffee and eating my cookie. Suddenly I felt something sc-r-runch between my teeth. I came very near getting it in my throat and choking to death—and that molasses cookie came from *you*," barked the Collector. He pointed his cane right at Mrs. Simonsen.

"Has the Collector found a doll in his molasses cookie?" cried Mrs. Simonsen in dismay.

"Exactly, Mrs. Simonsen—a doll in my molasses cookie. Disgusting—to say the very least!"

Then there was a great to-do! They called Schulze from

the bake-house. In his baker's cap and apron, he stood there jabbering German and insisting that he knew nothing about the doll. The Collector scolded and scolded. Mrs. Simonsen never got any further than to say, "But, your honor, your esteemed highness—" before the Collector interrupted her with, "Keep still, I say. It is I who will talk."

Oh, how frightened I was! Several times I was about to spring in and say that the doll was mine and that it was I who had put it in the dough, but I was afraid to.

"I will give you notice, my good woman, that hereafter no cookies for me shall be bought here," said the Collector. He struck his cane on the floor with great emphasis.

When he said that, I felt so sorry for Mrs. Simonsen and kind Heinrich Schulze, that before I knew it, I was in the bakery.

"Oh, it was I who did it! It was I who put the doll into the dough—just for fun—just for a joke on Schulze. Oh, please forgive me! I have been so sorry about it—oh, boo-hoo-hoo!" I threw myself down across the counter and lay there, sobbing, overwhelmed with relief to have told at last.

"Well, I must say!" exclaimed the old Collector, but his tone and manner had changed. "Is it here we have the culprit? And you did that for fun? For *fun?*"

"Yes, I thought Schulze would find it right away," I sobbed.

"H'm, h'm." The Collector cleared his throat. "Well, well. Let it pass, my good Mrs. Simonsen. I shall, after all, go on buying my molasses cookies here. They are exactly to my taste. And you, child"—he tapped my head with the silver head of his cane—"you must find some other kind of fun than putting dolls into molasses cookies for people to choke on." With that the Collector stamped heavily out of the shop.

Mrs. Simonsen was upset with me and so was Schulze. I was only too glad to have the doll in my hands again. I was glad that no one had died from it. I was glad that I had eased my conscience by confessing. Oh, I cannot say how glad I was!

"Please don't be angry," I begged. "I did it just for a joke, you know. I will never, never do anything like that again."

"Well, indeed, you had better not, young lady," snapped Mrs. Simsonsen.

"Well, indeed, you had better not, young lady," repeated Schulze. But I caught a funny little twinkle in his eye as he glared at me. And he seemed to be having trouble keeping his mouth straight.

He went out the back door toward the bakery. I went home.

Somehow, since that time, I don't feel like going into Mrs. Simonsen's shop as often as I used to. But I still go into the backyard to see Schulze, though I scarcely ever get hungry for molasses cookies anymore.

# Bread Making

Mother's kneading, kneading dough,
In and out her knuckles go;
Till the sticky, shapeless lump
Grows a pillow, smooth and plump.

Then she cuts it, pops it in
To the neatly buttered tin,
Leaves it rising high and higher,
While she goes to make the fire.

How the glad flames leap and roar,
Through the open oven door;
Till their hot breath, as they play,
Makes us wink and run away.

When they've burnt to embers red
Mother shovels in the bread;
And that warm, delicious smell
Tells her it is baking well.

When it's golden, just like wheat,
We shall get a crust to eat;
How I wish we could be fed
Every day on new-made bread!

—E. L. M. King

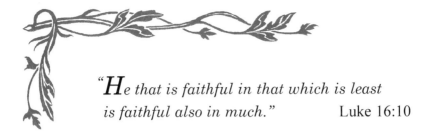

*"He that is faithful in that which is least is faithful also in much."* Luke 16:10

# The Best Recommendation

One afternoon more than a hundred years ago, a boy named Fred Morris ran into his house, calling for his mother. "Look here," he cried, holding out a newspaper. "A Mr. Johnson is **advertising** for an office boy. On Hickory Street. Only ten blocks away. I could walk to work. It says apply Wednesday at 10:00 o'clock. That's tomorrow.

"I asked someone what kind of work an office boy does," Fred went on. "He runs errands and empties wastepaper baskets and other little things like that. I'm sure I could do it. May I go and try for the job?"

Fred's mother took the paper and **briefly** read the ad. Then she handed it back. "Oh Fred, I wish you didn't have to go to work. But since Father died, I can hardly make ends meet. We've been praying for something you could do

to earn money. Maybe this is the answer."

"It says here, 'Letter of **recommendation** is **preferred**,'" Fred said with a frown. "What does that mean?"

"A letter of recommendation is a letter a grown-up friend writes for you to hand in when you apply for a job. He might say he knows you to be a good, honest boy who gets along well with others. Someone you worked for before could write a letter saying he knows you to be a hard work- er, or that you have experience in the same kind of job you are trying to get."

"Who could write a letter of recommendation for me?"

"No one," said Mother. "There wouldn't be time to get a letter from anyone where we used to live. We haven't lived here long enough for anyone to get to know you."

"Then I won't have much of a chance to get the job, will I?" said Fred, in a discouraged voice.

"It is true that few businessmen would hire a boy they know nothing about. But if this job is God's answer to our prayers, you will get it without a letter of recommendation," said Mother.

"So I will," Fred cried, brightening. "Now let's get my clothes ready. I mean to be there good and early. A dozen other boys will want this job, I expect."

The next morning, Fred arrived early at the address on Hickory Street. A lady at the desk pointed him to a door that bore the name of Mr. Johnson.

He entered a room filled with chairs. A few boys already **occupied** the front seats. A man behind a desk looked up briefly and told him to find a chair. Fred did so, noticing that most of the other boys held an envelope.

"Letters of recommendation," Fred said to himself.

From that moment on, the door opened and shut almost without stopping, letting in boy after boy. Before ten o'clock, a boy occupied every chair. And still they came, lining up around the wall.

Some boys looked scared. Others whispered and laughed among themselves, making remarks about each new boy who entered. One tall, well-dressed boy cast scornful glances at those around him, advertising the fact that he thought they were beneath him.

And all the time Mr. Johnson, with a half-smile on his face, sat gazing over the group. Every once in a while he briefly wrote something on a notepad.

Sometime later Fred found himself standing along the wall near the back. He scanned the room. "Must be nearly thirty fellows here, all hoping for this job," he said to himself.

White envelopes in hand, papers peeping from pockets, told Fred the same story. Most of the boys there carried a letter of recommendation. No wonder. That is what the newspaper said that Mr. Johnson preferred.

Suddenly the boy beside Fred whispered, "I ain't got no letter. And I ain't got no chance against this crowd, anyway." He slipped out the door. A number of others followed him.

Fred looked after them. *I may as well go too,* he

thought. But then he remembered Mother's words: "If this job is God's answer to our prayers, you will get it without a letter of recommendation."

Mr. Johnson stood. "Those who have letters will please bring them to me. If you have no letter, come and write your name and age on this piece of paper."

The tall, well-dressed boy rose swiftly and started forward. So did many others.

"Stand back! Don't push! Quit shoving me!" hissed the tall boy. He shouldered his way through the group pressing toward Mr. Johnson's desk. He stuck a handful of envelopes across the head of a little boy in front of him. "I have four recommendations, sir," he said as politely as he could while thrusting his elbow in the face of a boy trying to squeeze past him.

Fred and two other boys waited until the crowd had thinned. Then they stepped up to sign the paper.

"So you three didn't bring letters?"

"No, sir," Fred answered promptly. The other two shook their heads. All three then signed their names while Mr. Johnson waited in silence. Then they took chairs left by some of the boys who had gone out.

Mr. Johnson sat down and pulled the stack of letters toward him. Now no one whispered or laughed. All sat in dead silence, their eyes fixed on the man who occupied the chair behind the desk.

"He's not half reading them," Fred said to himself, as he saw the man briefly skim letter after letter. In less than five minutes Mr. Johnson laid the last one on the stack. Then he wrote on the notepad for another minute. At last he stood up.

"Interesting letters, gentlemen. I preferred letters of rec-ommendation. Most of you brought one. That is good. Naturally, an office boy must follow directions."

"I brought four, sir," interrupted the tall, well-dressed boy.

Mr. Johnson acted as if he had not heard.

Fred sighed. "Well, that settles that," he said to himself.

Mr. Johnson continued. "According to the letters I just read, most of you would make excellent office boys. However, I need only one. So if Fred Morris will come for-ward, the rest of you may go."

Fred just sat there, disbelief written all over his face. There had to be a mistake. He looked around. There must be another Fred Morris. But no other boy made a move, so he slowly stood.

The tall, well-dressed boy jumped up. "Mr. Johnson, that's not fair. You were advertising for a boy with recom-mendations. I had four. That boy had none."

"You are mistaken about that," replied Mr. Johnson with a smile. "He had more than ten that I noticed. Sit down, and I will tell you about them."

He turned and picked up the notepad from his desk. "The first recommendation Fred Morris brought was that of good habits. He wiped his shoes on the mat when he came in. It's not muddy outside today. He wiped them out of habit—a good habit for an office boy.

"Next, he pays attention to small details. I learned that from the quiet way he closed the door behind him. That door always closes hard, but he made sure it was latched.

"He has a kind and unselfish heart. He gave his seat to that boy with a limp even though he had to stand the rest of the time. That showed me he keeps his eyes open for people he might help. Helping others is what an office boy does all day long.

"Fred looked as nervous as the rest of you, but he held his cap quietly after he took it off. He didn't twirl it or slap it on his knee like some of you did. That told me he could control himself. And he showed good manners by not attracting attention to himself by unnecessary noise and commotion."

Mr. Johnson glanced at the notepad and went on. "Some boys left when they realized most of you had letters and they didn't. Others left when they saw how many other boys hoped to get the job. Fred Morris did not leave, though I could tell he felt like leaving. That showed me he is willing to finish what he started, even when he had little hope of success.

"When I called for your letters and the names of those who didn't have any, Fred stood aside and waited. He didn't push or get angry when others got ahead of him. That proved he wasn't rude or easily upset.

"When I asked a question, he answered 'No, sir,' rather than shaking his head. That recommended him as polite.

"When he signed his name, I noticed his neatly combed hair and clean fingernails. His clothes may be a bit shabbier and more worn than some of yours, but they are clean and pressed. His shoes are shined, which shows he is neat and clean and that he isn't ashamed of what he can't help."

Mr. Johnson looked at his notepad again. "Yes, I preferred recommendations. Fred Morris brought more than a dozen with him. They tell me he will make a first-rate office boy. His actions told me more than all the written letters of recommendation he could have brought me."

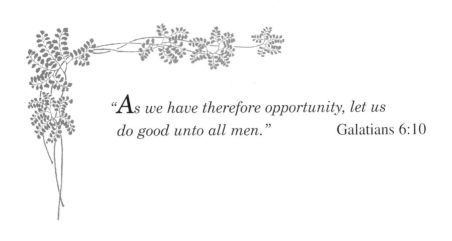

*"As we have therefore opportunity, let us do good unto all men."* Galatians 6:10

# The Surprise Package Company

"If we don't soon think of something, we will waste this whole summer," declared Conrad, as he hung up the tea towel.

Regina pulled the plug in the sink and watched the water swirl down the drain. "I know," she agreed. "School has been out for three weeks and we haven't done one thing. Mother, don't you have a good idea?"

"I think you have been busy enough," said Mother. "You do your chores. You mow the yard. You keep the garden and flower beds weeded. You help me with canning and freezing."

"But that's work," **protested** Regina. "We want to do something that's fun, like being a **detective** and solving a mystery."

"Yes," added Conrad, "or dangerous secrets to keep—like the early Anabaptists had to keep when the **authorities** tried to catch them. I read the best book about that."

Mother smiled. "I am sure you would not enjoy the dangers and fears of the Anabaptists. Being an Anabaptist was not fun. They suffered terribly sometimes. And I have no ideas for dangerous secrets for you to keep. You will have to invent such things for yourselves."

> **Who Were the Anabaptists?**
> (an ə bap′ tists)
>
> The Anabaptists were Christians who lived in the 1500s and later. They were hated and killed by many people because they determined to live the way God wanted them to.
>
> The governments of many countries tried to keep them from believing and teaching God's Word by putting them into prison, torturing them, and putting them to death.

"All right, we will," said Conrad promptly. A sudden gleam of excitement shone in his eyes. "May we do anything we please?"

Mother laughed. "Of course not. You can't do anything you know I would forbid if I knew it."

"But we don't have to tell you what we are doing, do we?" Regina could tell her brother had gotten one of his good ideas. "It would be much more fun if we kept things secret. Detectives don't tell what they know. That would be a sort of mystery, at least to you."

"No, you don't have to tell me, But don't forget, mothers are pretty good detectives themselves. Only you will have to answer any questions I decide to ask you if I think you are doing something questionable."

"Oh, sure. We'll do that," promised Conrad. "Come on, Regina, I've got a great idea!"

That afternoon, Mother needed to go to town. The minute her car disappeared down the road, Conrad and Regina rushed to carry out their first plan.

"I'll get to the dishes," said Regina. "Do you think you could wash the windows outside? You'll need the step-ladder."

"Sure, if you show me how," Conrad replied. "I'll fetch the ladder. You round up the stuff I'll need."

"We'll have at least an hour," **surmised** Regina. "It always takes her that long to get groceries."

How the two hurried! Regina washed and dried dishes and put them away. She wiped the table and counters, and swept and mopped the floor.

Conrad washed the windows inside and out. He emptied the trash can and took out the garbage. He shook the rugs and set the table for supper.

Just as he put down the last glass, he looked out the window for the twentieth time. "Here she comes!" he hissed. "Let's get out of here!"

"The note! The note! Don't forget the note!" Regina whis-pered **urgently.**

Conrad pitched a white envelope onto the counter and tiptoed after his sister. He eased the screen door shut behind him. Then they both leaped off the back porch and dashed around the corner of the house. In a **secluded** spot behind the lilac bushes they collapsed on the ground, laughing and gasping for breath.

After a few minutes they returned to the kitchen. Mother stood there staring all around.

"Did Aunt Martha come when I was gone?"

"No. Not that we saw," said Conrad.

"Did Sister Hannah come? No, she wouldn't come here and do such a thing." Mother answered her own question.

"Anyway, what a lovely thing for someone to do. Now I can sit and rest till time to get supper. But I do wonder who did it."

"Hey, look. Here's a letter," cried Conrad, picking up the envelope. Maybe it says who did it."

Mother opened the note and read aloud, "'The Surprise Package Company wishes you a very pleasant afternoon.' Now who in the world is the Surprise Package Company?" Mother glanced at Conrad and Regina but they had turned to take things from the grocery bags. Neither looked up or offered to answer her question.

When Daddy came home from work, Mother showed him the note and told him about the spotless kitchen.

"The Surprise Package Company," he mused. "I never heard of a company by that name around here." He looked keenly at Conrad and Regina.

"Sounds like a funny company to me," remarked Conrad. He did not look at Daddy or Regina.

"The Surprise Package Company," repeated Regina.

"They didn't leave any package for Mother." But she didn't look at Daddy or Conrad.

A few days later, after the children had washed the breakfast dishes, they waited until Mother went to the basement. Regina slipped out the back door and motioned urgently for Conrad to follow. He paused only long enough to grab a package from under the lilac bush. Then the two disappeared into the cornfield.

How secluded and safe they felt as they went single file down a row toward the woods. The broad green blades of the corn rustled all around them, while the tasseled stalks stretched above their heads.

"Couldn't we get lost in here?" asked Regina, after a bit.

"No. Not if we stick to this row," Conrad reassured her. "It is bound to come out on the road. I was just thinking how Anabaptists had to hide sometimes. I don't think they had cornfields though."

"Did you think Mother looked at us funny when we said we needed a jar of grape juice for a project?" asked Regina.

"I didn't look at her," said Conrad, with a laugh. "I was just hoping she wouldn't ask any questions."

Before long the children came to the road through the woods at the end of the cornfield. Not far away in a secluded little clearing they could see Mr. Rollins' house. The old gentleman lived alone. He could do most things for himself, but spent a lot of time dozing in his rocking chair.

"Oh, I do hope he is sleeping," whispered Regina. "What will we do if he isn't?"

"You don't have to whisper," said Conrad. "He can't hear us this far away. Besides, he's hard of hearing.

"If he isn't sleeping, we could put it on the doorstep, then knock and run. But he can't see very well and could stumble over it."

"Well, if we put it off to the side, he might not see it for days and days. If it rained, it would wash off the note. Do you think we wrote it large enough for him to read?"

"I think so." Conrad held the package at arm's length. "God bless you today. With love from the Surprise Package Company," he read.

"Let's just pray that he'll be sleeping. Then we can slip in and leave it on the table. Sometimes the Anabaptists escaped by praying that God would make their guards go to sleep. So I'm sure God can make Mr. Rollins be asleep too."

"But we're not Anabaptists," objected Regina.

"We can pretend we are," returned Conrad. "And since we're doing something good, I think God will answer us."

As they neared the house, they left the road and circled into the woods, approaching from the back. Regina waited off to the side, while Conrad stepped to the window and peeped in. He turned with a wide grin and motioned urgently. "Sleeping," he mouthed.

Regina hurried to the door and slowly turned the knob. It opened easily, but creaked alarmingly as the two stepped in.

Old Mr. Rollins sat in a rocking chair with his chin on his chest, his eyes closed.

Quietly Conrad moved to the table and set the package on it. As he stepped away a floor board protested with a loud creak.

Mr. Rollins stirred and raised his head. "Wha-a-a-t? Who's there?" he quavered drowsily.

But Conrad had reached the door. Regina closed it silently behind him. Together they darted into the woods and popped behind broad tree trunks. After waiting a while, they circled back to the road and entered the cornfield.

"That was close," breathed Regina. "Do you think he saw us through the window?"

"Oh, no. He can't move that fast. He's probably still sitting there trying to decide if he heard anything," Conrad surmised. "Now let's get back to the house. Mother might be needing us for something. If not, we'd better get to work on our next project."

One week not long after that, all the older ladies of the church received a greeting card. A pressed wildflower and a tiny spray of ferns decorated the outside. Inside they read:

**Not a birthday**
**Not a holiday**
**Just a HAPPY DAY card.**

**"This is the day which the LORD hath made;**
**We will rejoice and be glad in it." Psalm 118:24**

**—From the Surprise Package Company**

Several days later Conrad and Regina worked all evening on the floor in a corner of the dining room. They paged through old magazines and newspapers. They cut and pasted, laughed and whispered.

"Keep your eyes open for *good*. I need *good* and *before* and *pig*," said Regina.

"OK. And you watch for *bicycle* and *night*, and *expect* and *good-bye*."

Finally Daddy said, "Don't you think you should begin cleaning up your mess? How much longer is it going to take you?"

"We only need a few more words," Regina replied.

"We'll be done in ten minutes," promised Conrad. "Come on, Regina. Let's just spell them out letter by letter."

Before long Daddy heard Regina's joyous squeal. "Ten feet long! It's ten feet long, Conrad. That will make a real package, especially if we put in you-know-what. But how will we get it to him? We don't have the money to send it in the mail."

"Sh-h-h-h-h," warned Conrad, with a frown and a nod toward Daddy.

Several days later Conrad and Regina had run out of ideas. They could think of no way to get their ten-foot letter to Eric Taylor. Eric did not attend their church, but Conrad had heard he had rheumatic fever and had to stay in bed for weeks and weeks.

"I'll just have to take it to him," he decided.

"You can't walk that far," said Regina.

"I'll go on my bike. It's not on a busy road. But I'll have to ask Mother and Daddy, of course."

The children had learned long ago that their parents were good detectives and caught on to most of the projects of the Surprise Package Company. They didn't really care. However, they still did their best to keep their activities secret.

Mother wasn't too eager for Conrad to go, and Daddy said, "You are forgetting the hills between here and there. You'll get awfully tired."

"I don't care," said Conrad. "I'll just think about how tired the Anabaptists must have been when they had to leave their homes to flee to another country. Only they didn't have bikes to ride. I'll pretend I'm one of them."

"Well, all right," Mother finally agreed. "But I will call Mrs. Taylor and explain things. I don't want you trying to sneak up to their house without being seen."

"But then they'll know who it's from," protested Conrad and Regina together.

"I'll ask her not to tell Eric who brought it. And she can say which door to come to, so he won't see you."

Mother came back from the phone chuckling. "It's a good thing I called or you really would have had some Anabaptist experiences. Mrs. Taylor said their dog never would have let you inside their yard. She's going to tie him up. And you are supposed to come to the front door."

Later, at the supper table, a weary Conrad reported his adventures while going to Eric's house.

"You were right about those hills, Daddy. I had to get off and walk to the top a couple of times. But it was worth it going down.

"I delivered the package and never even saw the dog. Mrs. Taylor thanked me and gave me two doughnuts."

"So you had no Anabaptist experiences, after all," commented Daddy.

"Well, actually, I did have one. But I sure wasn't thinking of Anabaptists while it was happening."

"What happened?" gasped Regina.

"Well, on the way home a Doberman chased me. He was different from the other dogs that had come out and barked as I went past. This one took after me! When he first dashed out, he startled me so badly I almost wrecked. He meant business!

"I was going downhill, so I got ahead of him. But he kept right on coming. I didn't know what I was going to do when I got to the bottom and started up the other side."

"Oh, weren't you scared?" breathed Regina, clasping her hands. "Didn't you pray?"

"Of course I prayed," said Conrad. "I was never so scared in my life. What scared me the most was that he just kept coming, even though I was way ahead of him.

"Then I heard a car horn. When I looked back, a car had stopped between me and the dog. A man got out with a stick. The dog must have been his because when he opened the car door, the dog jumped in."

Regina let out her breath in a long sigh.

"On the way home, then, I thought maybe that was a little bit the way Anabaptists felt when the authorities chased them to kill them, and how they prayed."

Then Daddy said, "Don't forget, Conrad, the Anabaptists didn't always escape. And they weren't always running from those who hated them. They lived peacefully and loved others by doing many things for them. I think what you and Regina are doing in your Surprise Package Company is more like the Anabaptists than you realize."

# Neighboring

The dear old woman in the lane
　Is sick and sore with pains and aches,
We'll go to her this afternoon,
　And take her tea and eggs and cakes.

We'll stop to make the kettle boil,
　And brew some tea, and set the tray
And poach an egg, and toast a cake,
　And wheel her chair round, if we may.

–Christina G. Rossetti

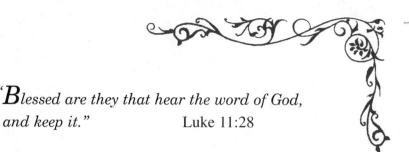

*"Blessed are they that hear the word of God, and keep it."* Luke 11:28

# Sower, Seed, and Soil

⁴ And when much people were gathered together, and were come to him out of every city, he spake by a **parable**:

⁵ A sower went out to sow his seed: and as he sowed, some fell by the way side; and it was trodden down, and the **fowls** of the air devoured it.

⁶ And some fell upon a rock; and as soon as it was sprung up, it withered away, because it lacked **moisture**.

⁷ And some fell among thorns; and the thorns sprang up with it, and choked it.

⁸ And other fell on good ground, and sprang up, and bare fruit an **hundredfold**. And when he had said these things, he cried, He that hath ears to hear, let him hear.

⁹ And his disciples asked him, saying, What might this parable be?

¹⁰ And he said . . . ¹¹ Now the parable is this: The seed is the word of God.

¹² Those by the way side are they that hear; then cometh the devil, and taketh away the word out of their hearts, lest they should believe and be saved.

¹³ They on the rock are they, which, when they hear, receive the word with joy; and these have no root, which for a while believe, and in time of **temptation** fall away.

¹⁴ And that which fell among thorns are they, which, when they have heard, go forth, and are choked with cares and riches and pleasures of this life, and bring no fruit to perfection.

¹⁵ But that on the good ground are they, which in an honest and good heart, having heard the word, keep it, and bring forth fruit with patience.

–Luke 8

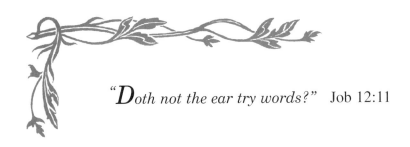

*"Doth not the ear try words?"* Job 12:11

# Spelling Bee to Spelling Book

"Come to my house to a spelling bee and taffy pull Friday night at candlelighting."

Blue eyes and brown turned toward the tall, slender boy with a high forehead and dark red hair who had given the invitation.

It was recess time in a bare country schoolroom in America, in the year 1770. No wall maps, pictures, or bookshelves made the room pleasant. No pictures in the schoolbooks made learning interesting. The fireplace in the room **scorched** the faces of those near it and left those a few feet away shivering.

If those students could have seen into the **future** and peeped into your classroom right now, they could not have believed their eyes.

How could a schoolroom be light all the time in every

corner whether the sun shone or not?

How could it be possible for everyone to be warm all the time with no fireplace?

How could each pupil have his own place to sit with books, paper, pencils, pens, crayons, a ruler, and scissors all his own?

But of course those students could not look into the future, so they learned in the only school they had. Cheerful pupils had a good time. Grouchy students grumbled just as they do in your schoolroom.

After recess, lessons were no longer **tedious**. There was high excitement at the thought of another spelling contest and taffy pull at Noah Webster's house. Everyone **admired** their serious, twelve-year-old classmate.

With swinging lanterns, they gathered from all directions that Friday evening. Upon their arrival at the Webster home, the young guests found a half-circle of vacant chairs arranged before the fireplace. When the boys and girls took their places, the flames from the great logs shone upon happy faces. Spelling at the Webster home was a jolly party, not a tedious task.

Noah's younger sister and brother sat with the guests. Noah stood opposite them, his back to the fire. He wore a **comical** stern-teacher look until the smell of scorched wool made him hastily step away from the flames. However, he continued to look serious, for he considered spelling very important.

The delightful odor of boiling taffy came from a huge

kettle over the fire. Frequently Jerusha stirred it to keep it from scorching. But the real business of the evening had everyone's attention.

"*Color*," Noah pronounced and motioned to Rebecca Hooker. She sat in the first chair next to Noah's sister.

"*C-o-l-o-u-r*," Rebecca answered.

"Wrong! Leave the circle," said Noah.

The other children giggled. They all knew why Noah had put Rebecca out of the circle. The schoolmaster taught them to spell in the British manner—*c-o-l-o-u-r*, and *n-e-i-g-h-b-o-u-r*.

But Noah Webster believed that the better way of spelling words like *color* and *neighbor* was the simpler New England way—without the *u*.

Noah passed the word to Jerusha. "*C-o-l-o-r*," she spelled as she moved into Rebecca's vacant chair.

The spelling bee continued, but there was nothing tedious about it. Noah gave out words familiar to the New England people: *stall, cupboard, rescue, pitch, soul, opossum, mischief, cousin.*

Finally only Jerusha remained. All the other children had missed a word. They did not mind. What else could be expected, they thought, from a girl who has Noah Webster for a brother!

Now came the more interesting part of the evening. With a piece of black, charred wood, Noah drew a comical picture of a bear on the pine walls of the kitchen. As he drew, he told an interesting story about the picture and wrote the more difficult words on the wall.

Noah's schoolmates crowded about him and admired his drawings. Because of the story and the picture, they could easily remember the spellings of these words.

Before long Noah had almost covered the kitchen walls with pictures and words. Then they scrubbed the pine boards, but the words remained clearly in the minds of those boys and girls. They enjoyed learning by Noah's way of teaching.

Now the party grew noisier. They pulled the taffy and ate it. They drank cider and played games until the Websters' tall grandfather clock struck nine.

Then the guests began putting on their wraps and telling Noah and his family how much they enjoyed the evening. Soon they departed, their lanterns in their hands. Walking along the dark roads in the bobbing light of their lanterns, they talked about the high prices they had to pay for schoolbooks.

"I shall have no new shoes all winter," Rebecca said sadly. "That's because Father had to buy me an arithmetic and a Bible for school. Books should be cheaper."

"I reckon Noah is smart enough to make a book," said Betsy Hand. "He knows so many words. He draws good pictures too."

"Noah make a book? You must be out of your wits!" William Duke exclaimed.

The others agreed. Noah Webster could draw pictures that certainly made spelling fun. But no one with any wits at all would think that their classmate could write a book. What a comical idea!

But they would not have laughed if they could have seen into the future, for Noah did write a book. When they grew up, their own children used a spelling book that Noah Webster had written.

The book contained lists of words used every day by American boys and girls. It also contained pictures and stories that helped pupils remember the words. When the children used this book, they enjoyed learning to spell.

Settlers who moved away from New England took thousands of Webster spellers to all parts of the country. They took them west, south, and north. They took them on stagecoaches, covered wagons, oxcarts, puffing little steam trains, and riverboats.

Meanwhile, Noah Webster himself traveled from farms to villages, and from villages to towns, explaining his speller to the teachers. Soon he carried with him another book, a dictionary that he had made. It, too, had pictures to help explain the meanings of words and showed how the words were pronounced.

With his speller and his dictionary, Noah taught countless boys and girls who lived far beyond the kitchen walls of his New England home.

Hundreds of years ago, long before Noah Webster, there were no rules for spelling. Each person spelled words in the way he thought was right. That meant that often the same word was spelled different ways by different people. Even a little word like *good* was once spelled in as many as 13 different ways!

Here are some examples of some ways people once spelled:

smoak (smoke)    boocke (book)

ellevene (eleven)    Ennglisshe (English)

As the years passed, men wrote dictionaries and made rules for spelling. People began to use the same spellings for words. Then Noah Webster came along. He didn't like the British spellings. He thought they were too hard. He thought Americans should use easier spellings. In his dictionary, he used "American" spellings.

Today, because of Noah Webster, some American and British spellings are very different. If you would read books printed in England, here are some words you might see:

tyre (tire)    waggon (wagon)    gaol (jail)

centre (center)    kerb (curb)

# Banananananananana

I thought I'd win the spelling bee
  And get right to the top,
But I started to spell *banana*,
  And I didn't know when to stop.

– William Cole

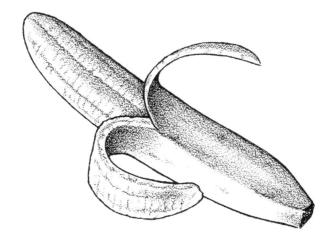

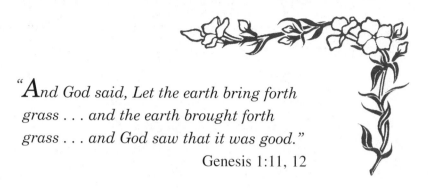

*"And God said, Let the earth bring forth grass . . . and the earth brought forth grass . . . and God saw that it was good."*

Genesis 1:11, 12

# Long Before Tractors

Brad and his little sister, Brenda, enjoyed the barn more than any other place on Uncle Tim's farm. In the city where they lived, they **seldom** had such interesting things to do as they did in the country. There they climbed ladders and hunted for eggs. They watched Uncle Tim milk the cows and feed the horses. They approached the goose's nest as close as they dared while she stretched out her neck and hissed at them.

But the most fun of all was playing in the hay. They scrambled up and then slid down the huge pile of hay in the loft.

Best of all, they could jump off a high beam in the loft and land in a sweet, dusty **smother** of hay. They sank way down in when they landed, getting hay down their necks and in their hair. In spite of this, Brad and Brenda liked jumping in the hay more than anything else. Seldom did a day pass but that they dashed up the barn **ramp,** climbed the ladder to their beam, and leaped off.

In May when Brad had gotten out of school, and they had come to the farm, there had been a fine high pile of hay to jump into. But as the days went by, that and many other things changed on the farm. They saw the duck pond **dwindle** to a pool and then to a puddle. The little chicks lost their coats of yellow fluff and grew white feathers. And the children noticed from their high jumping beams above the hayloft that the pile was getting farther and farther below them.

They knew Uncle Tim and Jake, the hired man, threw down great forkfuls of hay to the horses and cows every evening. But they never thought that the hay piled there in such huge shadowy mounds could ever dwindle to nothing.

But there was no doubt about it. Here and there they could see the board floor through the hay. One day when Brad jumped off his favorite beam, he hit the floor underneath the hay when he landed. That put an end to jumping in the hay.

"We don't have much more hay," Brad told Jake one evening. "It's getting time to order more from wherever you get it."

"We can't jump on it anymore, and the pile's too low to

slide on," added Brenda. Then she realized that Jake might not think it very important for them to have hay to jump and slide in. So she added, "Pretty soon the horses won't have any hay to eat, Jake. What will you feed them then?"

Jake said, "Ice cream," and winked at Brad.

"Oh, Jake," Brenda cried. "Horses don't like ice cream."

"How do you know they don't?" asked Jake seriously.

"They like apples and sugar," admitted the little girl, "so maybe they do like ice cream. But it would take a lot, Jake, and it would hurt their teeth. I want to know what you really would feed them."

"Jelly beans."

"He's just joking, Brenda," said Brad. Then he turned to the hired man. "Seriously, Jake, where do you get a whole barnful of hay, and how do you get it up in the loft? We have to go up the ladder. But you couldn't carry that much hay up the ladder."

"Keep your eyes open and you will find out," Jake answered.

The next morning the sun rose hot. Brad and Brenda headed down the lane to see where Uncle Tim had gone to work. They found him riding around the edge of a field of tall green grass, seated on a machine pulled by two horses. The machine had a long knife that cut down the grass and left it lying in flat rows. The children climbed on the fence under a tree and shouted to him.

When the horses came near, Uncle Tim stopped them. He pulled a big red handkerchief from his hip pocket and

wiped his face, and called, "Want to ride with me on the mower?"

Both children leaped off the fence.

"One at a time. Ladies first. Come, Brenda. Brad, I'll take you the next time around. Look out for the knife, Brenda."

Brenda ran over the soft piles of freshly cut grass to

Uncle Tim, who lifted her up in front of him on the iron seat. Off they started with the mower making a loud clattering noise. Brenda had to wrinkle her nose and squint her eyes because of the dust from the grass and the glare of the sun. She watched the knife slide close to the ground cutting down daisies and sweet clover as well as grass. How sweet they smelled in the hot still air!

White butterflies danced over the tops of the grasses, with here and there a big brown one or one with yellow wings edged with black. The tall grass rustled like silk as the horses' feet tramped through it. On the fence a meadow lark sang its sweet song. By the time they got around the field, sweat streaked down the sides of Brenda's dusty face. Her hair stuck to her head.

Then Brad took her place on the mower and she again climbed the fence and sat on the top board in the shade.

"Whew! It's hot out there," Brad panted as he joined his sister on the fence after riding around the field. "How does Uncle Tim stand it out there in the blazing sun!"

The children watched as the mower clicked and clattered round and round the field. They watched the patch of tall grass in the center dwindle with each round. They watched till the last strip fell under the clicking blades.

For several days the mown grass lay drying in the sun and wind. After the dew had dried one morning, Uncle Tim drove the team into the field, pulling the rake. The horse rake had curved teeth like great steel claws. Uncle Tim rode the rake up and down the field instead of round and round, as he had done with the mower. The long curved teeth gathered up the grass in great bunches, then dropped it in a long row. Back and forth went the rake till the grass lay heaped in rows that Uncle Tim called **windrows.** Brad and Brenda sat watching until Uncle Tim had finished the field.

Again the field lay under the hot sun while the grass dried still further.

After that, Jake brought another machine called a *loader,* which he fastened to the back of a wagon with high open sides. Uncle Tim drove the wagon along the windrows. The teeth of the loader caught the grass in bunches and carried it up and dropped it into the wagon. Jake stood in the wagon bed with a long fork, spreading out the grass and packing it down.

Brad and Brenda bounced excitedly on the fence till Uncle Tim called them over and told them to climb up on the wagon beside him as he guided the horses.

"It picks up the grass just like hands," Brad cried, watching the loader clean up the windrows as they went along.

"I would like to ride up with the grass," cried Brenda. "It's like a slide going backward."

"You wouldn't like to be dumped into the wagon on your head," said her uncle. "See, the grass comes up so fast Jake can hardly stay on top as the wagon fills."

"If it covered him up, he would smother then, wouldn't he?" asked Brenda seriously.

"Oh, we'll try to be careful not to let him smother,"

Uncle Tim promised, just as seriously.

When the hay reached above the sides of the rack, Jake got down and unfastened the loader. Uncle Tim told the children they could ride on top of the load on the way back to the barn. Brad and Brenda needed no second invitation, but clawed their way to the very top of the high pile.

"Isn't this fun!" exclaimed Brad.

"But it's sort of scary," Brenda quavered. "The whole load jiggles so, and there's nothing to hold onto. Let's make a hole and wiggle down where it's safer."

This they did. Then jiggling and swaying and rocking, they bumped along the field road, high above the backs of the sweating horses.

"Here we are," called Uncle Tim as the horses reached the ramp that led into the barn. After the children climbed down the sides of the rack, he said, "Now you may watch, but don't stand too close. The rope might break."

Brad and Brenda did not know what rope Uncle Tim meant, or why it might break, or what would happen if it did. They stood inside the barn door, out of the way.

The horses pulled the wagon into the barn. Then the men unhitched them, led them outside and fastened them to a rope that hung by the door. The rope went up to the very top of the barn through a pulley and to a great iron fork that hung there.

Though the children had played in the barn so often, they had never

**pulley**

noticed the big fork. Now Jake backed the horses until the big fork—which Uncle Tim called a *harpoon*—swung down and plunged into the grass on the wagon. It caught a great bundle in its iron **prongs**.

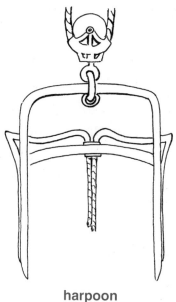

harpoon

"Go ahead!" he shouted, and Uncle Tim led the horses down the ramp away from the door-way. The rope tightened and up went the harpoon full of grass. Up, up it went, and then swung over above the empty hayloft.

"Whoa!" shouted Jake, and the horses stopped. Jake pulled another rope. The prongs of the harpoon opened, and down dropped the big bite of dried grass in a cloud of dust.

Uncle Tim backed the horses. Down went the harpoon to the rack to be filled again. Up it came and another big bunch of grass dropped on top of the first in the hayloft. Back and forth tramped the horses, seldom stopping for even a minute. Down swung the empty harpoon. Up it came full of dried grass, over and over. With every bite the load in the wagon dwindled and the pile in the loft grew larger.

Before long Jake and Uncle Tim hitched the horses to the empty wagon and headed back to the field to fill it again.

Brad and Brenda had not talked because there had

been too much to see. Now, in the quiet barn they slipped out of their corner and climbed the ladder to the loft where the men had dropped the load of grass.

"Brad!" gasped Brenda. "It's hay! That's where they get it. They cut the grass, bring it in here, and it's hay. Did you know that all the time?"

"I knew what they made hay out of, but I didn't know how they got it up here in the loft. Couldn't you tell by looking at it?"

"No. It looked like grass all the time. It didn't look like hay till I saw it up here in the hayloft. Just think, when they get the whole field in here it will reach clear to the roof."

"Plenty for the horses and cows to eat," said Brad.

"And plenty for us to jump and slide in the rest of the summer," added Brenda.

# Swallow Tails

I lie in the hay,
And watch the way
The swallows fly out and in all day.
From the hay on the floor,
The live-long day,
I watch the way
They swoop in and out through
    the old barn door.

In their nests of clay,
I hear them say
Whatever they say to the little ones there.
They twitter and cheep,
For that is the way,
Whatever they say,
The swallows put their children—and me—
    to sleep.

–Tom Robinson

# The Cornfield

I went across the pasture lot
When not a one was watching me.
Away beyond the cattle barns
I climbed a little crooked tree.

And I could look down on the field
And see the corn and how it grows,
Across the world and up and down,
In very straight and even rows.

And far away and far away—
I wonder if the farmer man
Knows all about the corn, and how
It comes together like a fan.

–Elizabeth Madox Roberts

# Farewell to the Farm

The coach is at the door at last;
The eager children, mounting fast
And kissing hands, in chorus sing;
Good-bye, good-bye, to everything!

To house and garden, field and lawn,
The meadow gates we swung upon,
To pump and stable, tree and swing,
Good-bye, good-bye, to everything!

And fare you well for evermore,
O ladder at the hayloft door,
O hayloft where the cobwebs cling,
Good-bye, good-bye, to everything!

Crack goes the whip, and off we go!
The trees and houses smaller grow;
Last, round the woody turn we swing,
Good-bye, good-bye to everything.

–Robert Louis Stevenson

# Autumn Fires

In the other gardens
　　And all up the vale,
From the autumn bonfires
　　See the smoke trail!

Pleasant summer over
　　And all the summer flowers.
The red fire blazes,
　　The gray smoke towers.

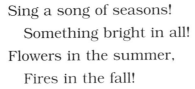

Sing a song of seasons!
　　Something bright in all!
Flowers in the summer,
　　Fires in the fall!

　　　　　　　　–Robert Louis Stevenson

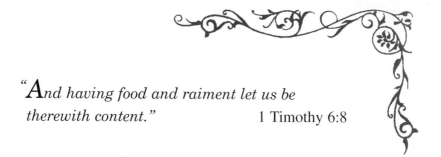

*"And having food and raiment let us be
therewith content."*  1 Timothy 6:8

# Cabbages to Calves to Cows

In 1650, the small Dutch town called New Amsterdam[1]
never dreamed it would one day become the great city of
New York.

In that village, noise always announced the end of the
school day. The Dutch mothers in the clean little Dutch
houses heard the clatter of wooden shoes on **cobblestones**.

"Here come the children!" they would cry. "Hurry the
dinner."

One Saturday a ten-year-old boy, Dirk Van Vos, walked
by himself. He frowned, decidedly cross, and kicked the
cobblestones with his wooden shoes. In New Amsterdam the
children went to school on Saturday—but only in the morning. On this Saturday afternoon Dirk wanted to go hunting

---

[1]Amsterdam – am′ stər dam

177

with the other boys for squirrels and rabbits. They would hunt with bow and arrow, like Indians.

"Vader[2] will want me to plant the cabbages after dinner when he goes back to his job at the docks," said Dirk to himself. "I'll be out there all alone till nearly dark. Why can't I ever have any fun?" He made his way to the last little house at the end of the cobblestown street.

As he entered the door, his mother, Vrouw[3] Van Vos, looked up from the kettle that she was stirring over the open fire. When she saw Dirk she cried out in surprise, "See the boy's face! Such a black frown! Never have I seen such a face on a boy before. It frightens me more than the painted Indians in this strange land."

But Dirk would not even smile at Moeder's[4] laughing words. He sat down quietly beside his father at the rough, wooden table. The clean little room held none of the bright cheerful things that the Dutch loved so well. No snowy tablecloth, no gay curtains, no tea towels, or other fine **linen** pieces like those he remembered from Holland. No blue-and-white teapot, sugar bowl, and cream pitcher. No shelves with cups and saucers and plates to brighten the room. Everything clean, but oh, so bare and ugly.

"Vader, may I go hunting with the other boys this afternoon?" asked Dirk.

"I think those young cabbage plants must be set out,"

---

[2]vader – vä′ dər: father
[3]vrouw – wife or Mrs.
[4]moeder – mü′ dər: mother

said his father quietly. Dirk's father talked little. Since they had come to New Amsterdam a year ago, it seemed to Dirk he had grown more silent than ever. Only Moeder's laugh made the bare little house cheerful and homelike. But Dirk did not think of his mother now. He had cabbage plants on his mind.

"Why do I have to work all the time?" he asked fretfully. "The other boys have time for some fun. I never do anything fun, and we never have anything!" Even as Dirk said the words, he wished that he could take them back.

Vrouw Van Vos turned from the kettle that she had been stirring, and Dirk could see her eyes fill with tears. She sat down heavily as she cried, "The boy speaks the truth! Oh, why did we ever **venture** to this new land? Why did we ever come to all this trouble?" She made a brave struggle to hold back the tears.

Dirk watched her, feeling worse by the minute. Never before, during all the hard times that they had been through, had he seen her cry. Now *he* had made her cry. She cried because he had complained about setting out cabbages!

Only a year had passed since the family had left Holland and ventured across the ocean to come to New Amsterdam. Only a year ago Herr[5] Van Vos had sold his fine farm in Holland, and Vrouw Van Vos had packed up her best linens in the big chest that she so treasured. She

---

[5]Herr – Mr.

had packed her blue-and-white china, the big feather beds, and her cooking pots and kettles. She had packed everything needed to make the new home in New Amsterdam bright and homelike.

Only a year ago Dirk had walked with his parents down to the dock to board the gaily painted ship with its big white sails. Dirk had run all over the boat, **investigating** every nook.

"How many sons have you, Herr Van Vos?" the captain had asked with a twinkle in his eye. "Everywhere I go I find a son of yours investigating my ship!"

Then the vessel sailed slowly out of the harbor. Even then Moeder had not cried. She had not cried, although they had left Dirk's two little sisters behind with Grandmother until they could make a home for them in the new land.

Hard times had followed the sailing of that ship. Before a week had passed, storms tossed it about the ocean. Many passengers became ill from the bad food and water and did not venture from their rooms for weeks. But the little ship struggled on toward the new world.

Then came the worst trouble of all. A winter storm drove the ship ashore on Long Island. All the people had been saved that dreadful night, but the ship had gone down with her cargo. Sunk was the great chest of fine linens that Moeder had woven. Gone were the feather beds and the dishes. Lost was the money that Vader had brought with him to buy a fine farm in New Amsterdam.

Fishing boats had picked up the passengers and carried them to New Amsterdam. The Governor, Peter Stuyvesant[6], had seen to it that each family from the wreck had a place to live. But all the passengers had to start over, with no money to buy what they needed. Dirk thought of the struggle of that long, hard winter as he watched his mother cry.

Suddenly Moeder sat up and wiped her eyes. "Shame on me," she said, "for crying like any silly woman! Here I have the best son and the best husband in all New Amsterdam, and I've not given either of them a bit of dinner!"

In another moment she put the food on the table, but Dirk could not swallow a bite. His mother reached under the table and patted his knee. "There, there, Son," she whispered. "Eat your dinner like a good boy. The day will come when we'll have cows in the barn and money in the money-box again."

"Our good God will see us through," said Vader. But his voice sounded tired.

Dirk slipped from his seat. "I'm going to set out the cabbage plants," he said.

All that afternoon Dirk carried tiny cabbage plants from the seedbed and set them out in long rows. His father's field lay at least a mile outside the wall that Governor Stuyvesant had built across the island to make New Amsterdam safe. Beyond the field where Dirk worked lay the pastureland. Every day the herdsman brought the cows

---

[6]Stuyvesant — stī′ ves ənt

from the town to graze there. Beyond the pasture the woods grew thick and wild.

Late in the day, Dirk stopped his work for a minute to rest his back and watch the cows in the pasture. Young calves ran beside some of the cows. They made him think of Holland and the fine herds that his father had once owned.

Dirk turned back to his plants with a fresh determination to work as hard as he could. Perhaps they could sell enough cabbages this summer to buy a calf. When it grew up it would have a calf, and then they would have two cows. Then they would have four cows, and then eight cows, and then a whole herd! He, Dirk, would take care of them himself.

"Cabbages to calves to cows. Cabbages to calves to cows." He began to chant it out loud as he went along tucking the plants into the soft soil.

Suddenly hearing a cry, the boy looked up and saw the herdsman in the pasture running and waving his arms and shouting. All the cows but one had lifted their heads and run toward the end of the pasture. What made them do that? He must investigate, for the herdsman seemed to be more interested in something at the other side of the pasture than in his fleeing cows. Dirk ran. He reached the herdsman, who pointed to a young calf that had ventured from its mother's side to the bushes at the edge of the woods. A dim yellow form crouched near it.

"A panther!" cried Dirk.

The calf gave a frightened *ma-a-a* and started away from

the edge of the woods toward its mother.

The herdsman began pouring powder and shot into his gun. Dirk caught up a stone as big as his two fists and ran forward. He threw it with all his might at the yellow shadow. At the same time, the cow, who had heard her baby's cry, lowered her horns, and charged the panther. The beast jumped aside, then sprang at the cow, sinking its fangs into its throat. The cow sank to her knees, bawling pitifully.

The herdsman ran in close and lifted his gun.

"Shoot! Shoot!" cried the boy.

Suddenly the calf turned and tried to join its mother. Without a second thought, Dirk dashed for the little animal. He threw his arms around its neck, and pulled it back.

Then came a flash of fire and the roar of the gun. The little calf trembled with fear, struggling to get away, but Dirk managed to hold her. Dirk saw both panther and cow drop to the ground where they struggled for a moment then lay still. He released the calf, which ran bleating to its mother. *Poor little thing!* thought Dirk.

The herdsman bent over the dead panther. "I'm glad I got that beast!" he said. "His skin will bring me a bounty from the Governor. Poor cow—she's done for, but I'm glad you saved the calf. She's a fine, strong one. It's a good thing you heard me shout."

"Who owned the cow?" asked Dirk.

"She belonged to Herr Van Cortland," said the man, "but he has plenty of others. Can you help me, lad? The whole silly herd has scattered through the woods. Can you spare some time to help me round them up?"

For an hour they worked, calling and investigating the thickets to find the frightened animals. At last they had them all gathered together. As the sun set, Dirk and the herdsman started back to the village, driving the cows before them. The calf wanted to stay with its dead mother, but Dirk finally got it to come along with him. It trotted close beside the boy, as he patted the lonely little creature and talked to it.

As the herd neared the wall, people hurried out to meet them. What had happened? Why were the cows so late? Again and again the herdsman told the story of the panther and the cow, and of how Dirk had saved the life of the little calf.

When Herr Van Cortland heard the tale, he complained at first. The panther had killed one of his best cows! She gave a lot of milk! She had the finest calves! But finally he remembered that he had many other cows. Then he looked at the little calf with Dirk standing beside it. The young animal began to bleat. Dirk patted it gently, and it put its nose in his hand, licking his fingers.

"Why, the boy has a way with the creature!" cried Herr Van Cortland. "Just look at how the calf takes to him. It will probably bawl all night for its mother. I have no time to raise an orphan calf. Can you feed it and care for it, my boy?"

"Yes, sir," answered Dirk eagerly, his eyes shining with pleasure.

"Then you may have the calf for your own!" declared Herr Van Cortland. "You saved it and you may have it! I do not have time to bother with it."

Dirk threw his arms around the little animal's neck in surprised delight. Then he remembered to thank Herr Van Cortland.

"I'll give you all the milk you need to raise it," cried a neighbor.

The people cheered as Dirk turned his calf down the cobblestone street toward home. He wanted to run, but the calf could not be hurried. It wanted to venture into every gateway. It wanted to investigate every dooryard they passed. And all the time Dirk wondered why his father and mother had not heard the shouting and come out to see what had happened. He found the door of the house closed.

Dirk burst into the room and saw his father and mother bending over a paper, reading it by the light of the fire. For a moment Dirk stood looking at them, too happy and excited to tell his surprise. The next moment, the calf, lonely and frightened, dashed into the room, knocking Dirk off his feet. Around the room it ran, *ma-a-a-ing* and sending bowls and kettles flying this way and that.

Dirk jumped up, soon cornered the calf and caught it.

"It's mine! It's mine!" he panted. Then he told the story as best he could.

"And now, the letter, the letter!" cried Moeder.

That afternoon, the first boat in many months had arrived from Holland. It brought a letter with news of Dirk's two little sisters they had left at home. And it brought other good news too.

"Your grandfather sent money to help us," explained Vader in a voice no longer tired. "We can build a barn, and your calf will start our herd. Good news brings more good news. In another year the little girls can come. I told you our good God would see us through."

The next thing Dirk knew, his mother had caught one of his hands, and his father had caught the other. Around the calf they skipped. Yes, even his silent, tired father was skipping! The house rang with laughter and happiness.

That night one tired Dutch boy drifted off to sleep murmuring, "Cabbages to calves to cows. Cabbages to calves to cows."

*"**F**or my thoughts are not your thoughts,
neither are your ways my ways,
saith the LORD."*         Isaiah 55:8

# The Mare That Heard a Voice

In the little village in the northwestern corner of Spain, everyone had gathered near the Pass of Pancorbo. Why did the people **accumulate** there? What caused such a festive occasion? The president? The Queen of England? Or some local hero?

None of these. A lowly, little dapple-gray mare named Pablita[1] had caused the festive occasion. A cart horse! What had an old cart horse done to deserve such honors? Read the following story and decide for yourself if she deserved the honor.

For years this little mare had pulled a cart filled with fruits and vegetables between two villages. A rugged moun-

---

[1] Pablita – pə blē′ tə

tain chain of jagged peaks and rock towers lay between the two villages. Every morning her master drove her to the local market and loaded up his cart. Then he peddled his produce in both villages—to one in the morning and to the other in the afternoon.

The peddler plodded through the narrow, winding streets cheerfully calling, "Apples! Peaches! Tomatoes!" Everyone liked him and admired his gray mare who followed him, faithfully pulling the cartful of fruits and vegetables. She waited as he chatted with a customer, then plodded along behind him when he moved on to the next.

Their **routine** seldom varied. Pablita knew her job and did it well. Not once in their many years together did she question her master's judgment.

A steep footpath over the top of the mountain had made travel between the towns very difficult. But some years before, the people had constructed a tunnel through the mountain between the two villages. Since then all the traffic took the much easier route. The tunnel was so narrow that only one line of vehicles could go through at a time. When traffic became heavy the last member of one group carried a signal flag and handed it to the last member of the group waiting to enter from the opposite direction. This kept the traffic in motion. From morning until night, cars, wagons, trucks, bicycles, carts—everything went through this narrow tunnel.

Late on the morning of July 2, 1968, old Pablita plodded according to their routine along the road toward the mountain. Her master drowsed on the high wooden seat behind her. He had sold everything in the one village and loaded up again. Now he dozed as the wagon creaked along. Soon they would go through the tunnel into the other village. If business was as brisk there, he would get home early.

Without warning, the cart came to a halt. He sat up, jolted into wakefulness. Why had Pablita stopped some distance from the tunnel entrance? He could see no **obstruction**. He slapped the reins across Pablita's back and clucked to her.

"Come on, little girl, we haven't got all day," he urged. She moved forward a couple of steps, then stopped again. This time she swung her head around and eyed her master. She seemed to be asking, "Are you sure you want me to keep going?"

The peddler frowned. He climbed down from the wagon and walked around Pablita, picking up each foot and examining it closely. Maybe a stone had become lodged in a hoof. There was no stone. He peered into the tunnel to see if there was an obstruction just inside the entrance. Or perhaps someone was approaching from the other end. Nothing. No obstruction. No one.

Climbing back into the wagon, he picked up the reins, and tapped the mare with his whip. Pablita trotted ahead a few paces, but when she reached the entrance of the tunnel, she stopped dead still.

Her master got down again. Catching hold of her bridle,

he tried pulling her forward—but Pablita did not **budge**. She planted her legs like four posts. The peddler tugged and jerked and scolded. The dapple-gray mare would not move.

By this time, the traffic had begun to accumulate behind them. People yelled and honked their horns, but the gray mare would not budge. Now the horse and cart blocked the entrance so effectively that nothing on wheels could get by, in or out. Someone ran through the tunnel to the other side of the mountain to explain the situation. "Don't come into the tunnel. You won't be able to get out, for the other end is blocked," he warned the people waiting there. Everyone knew it was impossible for anything to turn around inside the tunnel.

The peddler was really a gentle man, but the pressure building up behind him forced him to use his whip. The mare flinched but would not budge. A policeman came riding up on his motorcycle. When he heard about the problem, he quickly took charge. "Let's get some volunteers," he ordered. "You, you, you!" He assembled six or eight men around the mare. Together they tried to lift her off the ground. She did not fight them, but her feet seemed to have taken root.

"Unhook the wagon!" someone cried. "Then we can drag the old mare out of the way!"

The peddler unhitched the wagon, and the crowd rolled it off to the side of the road. Pablita still remained anchored in place. There was something **eerie** about the way she refused to enter the tunnel. What ailed her? The men gath-

190

ered around her again. Taking hold of the leather harness trailing down her sides, they began pulling. Pablita sat back on her haunches, braced for battle. As the tug of war began, everybody suddenly became aware of a strange **vibration**. The grunting of the men quieted. Everyone stopped and listened.

An eerie stillness hung in the air, almost as if the day were holding its breath. While the men stood like statues, the distant vibration began again. This time it rapidly grew stronger and stronger. The earth trembled beneath their feet. Then before their eyes, the inside of the tunnel exploded with a giant roar. The roof of the tunnel collapsed, sending great clouds of dust swirling out both entrances. The dust quickly enveloped Pablita, the men, and the scores of people and vehicles lined up behind them. The vibration rolled and boomed, then gradually subsided to a rumble, like distant thunder. As the dust settled, the men stood there, shocked but alive. In front of them the face of the mountain swept upwards unbroken. Every sign of the tunnel had disappeared.

Did Pablita know the cave-in was coming? She must have known. Did God tell her of the coming danger? Did He tell her not to enter the tunnel? Is that how He saved the lives of so many that day?

No wonder these Spaniards hold a celebration in honor of a little, dapple-gray mare. They believe that above the shouts of her master and all the angry men, she heard another voice.

*How many ways can you think of that the horse in this poem is different from Pablita?*

# Little Horse

This pretty horse
Is docile fire;
There's lightning
In his veins.

The little thunder
That you hear
Is hoofbeats
On the plains.

His mane and tail
Seem blown by wind,
Though not a breeze
Is blowing,

And puffs of dust,
Like springtime clouds,
Follow upon
His going.

—Elizabeth Coatsworth

# Burro With the Long Ears

FROM THE NAVAJO AMERICAN INDIAN

Ja-Nez—burro with the long ears—
Come with me to the water hole.
I will fill the kegs with water
And you will carry them home.
Down the crooked trail,
Through the deep hot sand,
Past the fragrant piñon trees,
Winding this way, winding that way,
Do not step into the cactus.
Now I wade into the water
Where it is clearest; I dip and pour.
While you drink I fill the kegs.
They are heavy as I lift them to your back again.
Now we wander through the cactus,
Past the fragrant trees,
Up the sandy trail, winding slowly.
At the hogan my mother sees
Us coming home with water.

–Transcribed by Hilda Faunce Wetherill

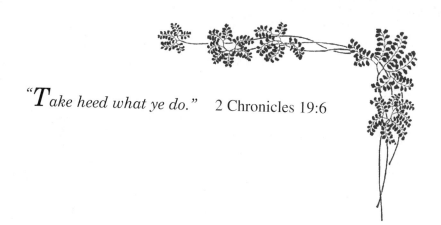

*"Take heed what ye do."*   2 Chronicles 19:6

# A Lesson That Stuck

Karen stood a moment holding her sled at the top of the hill, drinking in the beauty of the winter landscape. The snowy slope stretched below her, blue now, in the fading light. Ice **encrusted** the trees and fences so that they glittered orange in the glow of the sunset. She flung herself on her sled and swooped down one more time.

She had enjoyed sledding with her friends, but many of them had gone home, and she could feel her feet growing **numb** inside her boots. At the bottom of the hill she headed for home.

"It must be at least five below zero," she said to herself.

In upper Canada the temperature played an important role in everybody's life. Both her parents checked the temperature the first thing in the morning. Karen had learned to read the thermometer long before she could tell time.

Judging by the growing darkness, Karen knew it must be around three o'clock in the afternoon.

Suddenly she stumbled over an ice-encrusted stone in the middle of the path. Before she had time to **whimper**, she found herself flat on the snow with the sled riding up on her legs. "Pay attention to what you are doing," Karen scolded herself with the words she so often heard from her mother. Getting to her numb feet, she brushed herself off and went on.

Close to the place where her father worked she stopped. She leaned on the fence that separated the path from the parking lot and tried to spot her father's car among the others there.

Absentmindedly, she stuck out her tongue and licked the ice on the metal fence. Instantly, but too late, she remembered all the warnings she had heard. Her tongue was stuck, frozen to the fence. She screamed in her throat, terrified and angry with herself. Her parents had often warned that this could happen. Others had told stories about children who had to have their tongues cut off to get loose. Of course, she didn't believe the stories, but now they flashed through her mind, leaving her numb with terror. It was growing dark. No one would ever find her! She would have to stay there all night! Oh, if she had only paid attention to what she was doing and to the warnings she had heard!

"Hi, Karen, what's the matter?" asked a voice. Her friend Anders appeared beside her.

Karen could only whimper.

"You're stuck? Wait, don't move! I'll get you loose!" Anders cried urgently.

Karen had now lost all feeling in her tongue. Her feet and hands also had gone numb. The tears had begun to freeze on her cheeks. She knew in that temperature her tongue would soon have **permanent** damage.

Suddenly she heard Anders' pounding feet. She rolled her eyes sideways and saw he had a big glass of water in his mittened hand.

"I got this from Mrs. Stevens," he panted. Then carefully he began to pour the warm water down over Karen's tongue and the fence wire. In a moment her tongue came free. She reached for the glass and took a gulp, holding the warm water in her mouth until the numbness left her tongue.

"You'd better go home now," said Anders. "Next time, pay attention to where you put your tongue." He headed for Mrs. Stevens' house with the glass as if melting tongues off fences were something he did often.

Later, Karen sat comfortably at the kitchen table. She carefully sipped the hot chocolate her mother had made for her. Her tongue hurt so badly she could hardly keep from whimpering as the hot liquid flowed over the tender spot.

"What's the matter? Do you have a blister in your mouth?" her mother asked.

Karen's cheeks grew redder than the cold had made them. "Mama, do you remember the story you told me once about Aunt Elsa getting her tongue stuck on your gate

when you were small?" Karen's words came out very slowly and carefully.

"Yes, I remember," her mother answered. Suddenly it dawned on her what had happened.

"You didn't! We told you! Why didn't you pay attention..." Mama stopped when she saw the tears starting in Karen's eyes.

She leaned over the table. "Let me see. Stick it out," she said quietly.

Karen stuck it out.

"You poor child," said Mama after she was satisfied that there was no permanent damage. "It will be a while before that heals."

Karen told how it had happened and how Anders had saved her.

"It is the strangest thing," her mother said, "but it seems as though children just *have* to lick an icy fence or stick their tongue on some frozen metal once in their lives. You know, we really weren't that young when it happened to Elsa. She must have been around fifteen."

"Really!" Karen looked up in astonishment. "That old?"

"Yes, that old." said Mama. "And if she hadn't immediately cried out, I would have gotten stuck too, because I was just ready to try it myself. I remember we had a race to the gate. She got there first and got stuck. We had been warned never to do that, but she had this crazy notion that it would taste like ice cream. So she didn't pay any attention to what we had been told, just as you didn't."

"But Mama, why does your tongue stick? Other things don't."

"It's because your tongue is wet. The frozen metal turns the wetness to ice and there you are. If you took hold of the fence with a wet hand, it would freeze fast too."

"Would it, really?" Karen sat looking thoughtfully at her cup. Then she took the last swallow, easing the warm chocolate carefully over her sore tongue.

"Well, Mama," she said, setting down the cup with a bang. "After today, I won't have any trouble paying attention to that bit of information. I think this lesson will really stick."

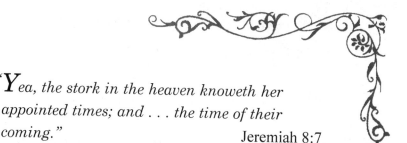

*"Yea, the stork in the heaven knoweth her appointed times; and . . . the time of their coming."*

Jeremiah 8:7

# Will the Storks Fly Home?

*Julie and her small brother Jon lived on a little farm in Holland. Each year in the spring, they eagerly watched for the return of the big white storks to their huge nest on the rooftop. This year Vader feared the storks would not come because of the great planes that were threatening Holland with war.*

An old wooden cuckoo clock hung on the kitchen wall. Every hour, a little blue-painted bird popped out of the door and whistled *cuckoo, cuckoo*. One morning, just as the cuckoo clock in the kitchen struck four, Jon crept quietly out of his cupboard bed and down the small ladder. His sister still slept in her own wall bed beneath him.

Jon pushed the curtains aside and tugged at the sleeve of her nightgown. "Julie," he whispered, "get up. It is time for the storks to come."

Julie opened her eyes in the darkness and could see nothing. Then she heard Jon whispering, and sat up, only half awake.

"We couldn't see them. It is too early, Jon," she answered drowsily.

"Shhh!" **cautioned** Jon. "No, it's not. Come on!"

So Julie eased out of her warm bed. She dressed quickly by the kitchen stove. They tried not to make a sound, for Moetje[1] and Vader were asleep upstairs. It would be a little while yet before Vader got up to milk the cows and Moetje came down to make breakfast.

**Donning** warm sweaters they slipped out the kitchen door. No living thing stirred. Nothing made a sound anywhere. High overhead the stars twinkled **serenely** in the sky.

Clutching each other, and not too **courageous** in the dark, Jon and Julie stumbled down the path until they reached the little wooden bench Vader had built for them under the pear tree. From there they could peer up at the rooftop. In the darkness they could barely see the outline of the storks' nest.

"Hello, you old long-**shanks**," called Jon, just as if he saw the storks.

"Hush," cautioned Julie. She knew that the birds had not arrived. They would not come in the night, because birds didn't fly in the dark. At least that's what she thought. And Vader said maybe they wouldn't come at all. Because

---

[1]Moetje – mü′ chə: mama or mommy

of the nearby war, airplanes filled the skies day and night sometimes. Perhaps the planes and booming of the guns would frighten the storks away.

Anyway she and Jon were quite courageous getting up in the dark all by themselves.

Suddenly, a rooster crowed. Julie jumped. Jon snuggled closer to her. "It was only an old rooster," he said. "I'm cold," he added suddenly.

"So am I," whispered Julie. "Do you want to go back to bed?"

"Oh, no!" Jon protested. And Julie was secretly glad.

So they clutched their sweaters snugly around their necks and huddled closer together.

As the sky lightened, the stars faded in the night sky. One by one they went out, like melting snowflakes.

Then from the barn came the low whinny of the fat horse that Vader drove to the village and hitched to the plow.

"That's Swisher," said Jon. "Swisher's awake." But he did not take his eyes from the storks' nest.

It seemed to Julie that the sun would never come up that morning. She hugged her slippered feet under her wide wool skirt to keep them warm. As the sky turned from gray to pale pink, the house door opened. Vader stepped out, donning his barn coat, and started down the path. When he saw the two small figures huddled side by side on the bench, his bushy eyebrows arched in surprise.

"What is going on here?" he asked, pretending to be

very cross. "You look like a couple of tramps waiting for breakfast. What are you doing?"

Julie and Jon ran to Vader as fast as they could. "We're waiting for the storks to come. Do you think they will?" they both said at once. Each clutched one of his arms and snuggled close. How good to see Vader standing there. They knew *he* wasn't afraid of the dark.

Vader tried to look very fierce. "If I were a stork I wouldn't fly through the sky with airplanes zooming and guns booming. But I'm not a stork." Then he burst into a hearty laugh that startled all the barnyard creatures. The ducks began to quack, the roosters crowed, and the cows in the barn mooed. Swisher neighed at the top of his lungs. Somewhere in the distance dogs started barking.

Moetje came to the doorway. "What . . ." she protested. Then she stopped. For there stood Vader with Jon hanging on one arm and Julie on the other, laughing together.

"It's daybreak, Moetje," he said in high good humor. "And here are two little tramps I found under the pear tree." With that he shook them both loose, and strode off toward the dairy to get the milk pails, chuckling as he went.

"We're waiting for the storks!" announced Jon. His round face dimpled and he laughed. Then Julie laughed.

Finally Moetje burst out laughing too. "Come now," she said. "Come get your chocolate and eat your breakfast."

But Jon protested, "Please, Moetje, let me stay out. I don't want any breakfast. Please . . . the sun is just coming up and the storks may come any minute."

"You obey your mother," called Vader as he came out with the milk pails and started for the cow barn. "Eat your breakfast. The sun has come up many times before, and it will come up again."

Jon went into the house without another word and climbed into his chair. "I must watch for the storks," he protested. "I don't want to miss them."

"My boy," Moetje said gently, as she hurried from stove to table with the cups and dishes, and gave the children big bowls of hot porridge, "you need to have patience."

"Anyhow, the storks will come sometime today," he insisted. "Won't they, Moetje?" He pulled a currant out of his coffee cake and popped it into his mouth.

"I do not know. Do not get your hopes up," cautioned Moetje. "Storks would have to be very courageous to fly through a sky full of war planes."

The sun climbed high in the sky, and the storks did not come. Jon wandered all over the yard, while Julie helped Moetje. Now and then she and Julie came out and walked down the sandy path. Moetje put up her hand to shade her eyes and scanned the sky, not saying much. She hung clothes on the line. She picked some pink hyacinths and put them in the little blue vase on the windowsill. Jon knew she was looking for the storks too.

At noon they ate dinner when Vader came back from the fields. Still the big white birds had not appeared. Even Vader glanced up briefly at the big nest as he came in from his work. "No birds yet?" he asked Moetje, with a little twinkle in his eye. He liked to tease Moetje, because she looked forward as eagerly as the children themselves for the coming of the storks.

"Oh, they'll be here—they have a long journey," Julie put in.

"How long a journey, Vader?" Jon wanted to know. "Where do the storks come from, anyhow?"

"Well, Son," said Vader, "there are at least seventeen different kinds of storks, so I've read. Our white stork flies all the way from Africa to get here in the spring. Many of them winter along the Nile River. That is, as Julie told you, a long, long way from here, but they have strong wings and a sure sense of direction."

"Yes, the good Lord created them so that year after year, when spring comes, they know how to return to the very same nest!" said Moetje.

The family finished dinner. Vader donned his boots and returned to his planting, but the big white birds still had not appeared.

At three in the afternoon, Jon grew discouraged and went to play. Julie sat by the window sewing serenely. Moetje said she must sew a little each day. So she was hemming a fine white cap to wear on Sundays, but she did not worry. She felt sure the storks would fly home in their own good time.

"Julie," Moetje said finally, "perhaps Vader is right. Perhaps, because of the war, they will not come this year."

"Do you think the war will come to our country,

Moetje?" asked Julie, looking up from her sewing.

Moetje's face saddened. She did not like to think about war. Germany was not far away, and the fighting Germans already occupied Belgium, France, Poland, and Austria. As she ironed the clean clothes and stacked them neatly, she said firmly, "We are a peaceful country, Julie. Holland does not have war. Our people work hard and mind their own business. I hope the storks will come, but the war—no—it must not come to the Netherlands."

"God will not let war come," remarked Julie serenely. "He will take care of everything."

Then Jon burst through the kitchen doorway shouting, "Julie, Moetje! Here they come! They're coming! I see them!"

The three rushed out into the April sunshine. Sure enough, there came the storks gliding over the treetops, over the blue canal, over the blossoms on the pear tree.

"How big they are!" marveled Jon. "And look at their long, red bills."

"How beautiful they are with black on their wings!" cried Julie.

And Moetje rejoiced, "I am so glad they have come again."

As the two big white birds flapped over the housetop, Julie and Moetje and Jon stood hand in hand, their faces lifted eagerly. Moetje's apron blew in the wind. Julie's yellow pigtails bobbed this way and that in her excitement. Jon waved one hand while he clung to Moetje with the other.

"Hello, you old long-shanks!" he shouted.

Moetje cautioned, "Gently, gently, do not frighten them!"

But Jon's shouts did not frighten the storks in the least. They had flown over many strange lands, and now, by some sure instinct, they knew they had reached home. The two big birds flew above the roof and snapped their bills,

making funny sounds like hand-clapping. They acted noisily delighted to find their old nest right where they had left it the autumn before. They circled it again and again. Then, with a great flapping of broad wings, they descended and alighted on the edge of the nest. Putting their heads together, they touched bills lovingly, and stretched their wings as though weary.

"Look, Moetje, they are the very same ones," cried Julie. "The ones from last year have come home again!"

Jon jumped up and down in great glee. "I will get them bread," he declared. "They are probably very hungry. May I get them some bread, Moetje?"

"Yes, they have come a long way. They have flown many thousands of miles from the south. They'd rather have frogs, snakes, and insects, but after their long journey they might be hungry enough to eat bread. Let's go get them some."

Julie lingered alone in the yard, her blue eyes lifted. She rejoiced in the miracle of the safe arrival of the huge birds. In her heart she had known all along that the storks would fly home.

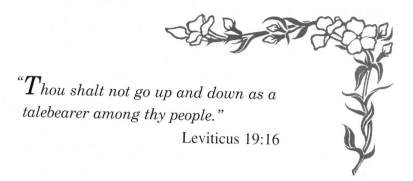

*"Thou shalt not go up and down as a talebearer among thy people."*

Leviticus 19:16

# Mystery of the Empty Lavoir

Plou-Las is a little town in Brittany. You pronounce it as if it were spelled *Ploo-Lah*. Nanette lived in Plou-Las with her grandmother, whom she called "Grandmere."

On a map of France, you can find Brittany in the northwest corner—the part that sticks out like a point.

Some housewives in Plou-Las washed their clothes on Monday. Others washed on Tuesday or Wednesday, and all the other days of the week, except Sunday. In Plou-Las all the housewives used the same washtub. Naturally they couldn't all use it at the same time. The tub was out in the field instead of in the kitchen, and they called it the Lavoir instead of the washtub. Pronounce Lavoir like this— lǝv-währ′. The Lavoir was a large stone-bordered pool. The

211

water ran in from a fountain nearby. When the pool filled, the water ran out an overflow pipe at the side. A wooden gate held the water in. You lifted the gate up to let the water out when the Lavoir needed cleaning.

Grandmere washed on Mondays. Early in the morning she bundled the wash into her big apron and called, "Come, Nanette! The earlier we reach the Lavoir, the cleaner the water will be."

This Monday, however, something very strange had happened. The Lavoir was nearly empty. Water trickled slowly in from the stone fountain, to be sure. But someone had raised the gate and let out the water. Why would anyone do that? Now the housewives who washed on Monday must wait till the Lavoir filled again, and that would take a long time.

"I cannot understand it," everybody said to everybody else, very **irritably**. "This has never happened before. The gate could not raise itself. A person raised it. Who did it?" They looked so angry that Nanette was glad she was not the guilty person.

"Perhaps the water **seeped** out through the gate," suggested Grandmere.

"No," they said. "Look at the water. None of it is seeping out now." Sure enough, a few inches of water stood in the Lavoir. None was running out below the gate.

"A naughty child did it," surmised someone. All the housewives **glared suspiciously** at everybody else's children.

"I didn't raise the gate!" said Nanette.

"I didn't either!" said her little cousin, Jean Pierre.[1]

"Neither did we," cried all the other children, clinging to their mothers' skirts.

Everybody **denied** it, yet the gate had been raised and the water released.

"Well." The housewives shrugged their shoulders. "Accidents happen sometimes." They began washing their clothes in the shallow water as best they could.

Early the next morning Nanette hurried down to the Lavoir. Again angry housewives stood around talking irritably to each other. The Lavoir stood nearly empty.

"This is too much!" they scolded. "Someone needs to do something about it! Someone's bad child came down here and raised the gate again. Which of you did it?" They glared around at the children who had gathered.

"Oh, no, we didn't," denied the children. "We were sound asleep in bed. How could we have done it?"

True. All the children had been fast asleep in their beds. Then who could have done it?

"Who do you think raised the gate?" Jean Pierre whispered to Nanette. He had come to stand beside his cousin when the housewives had begun talking so irritably.

"I can't imagine—I know I didn't," she whispered back.

"Me either," said Jean Pierre.

"Oh, Jean Pierre, let's find out who did," Nanette whispered excitedly.

---

[1] Jean Pierre – zhän pē′ er

"Us? How can we find out who did it?"

"We can steal out tonight and watch!" said Nanette. "Think how we will surprise everyone when we tell them who let out the water. You'll go with me, won't you?"

"Well, I guess," Jean Pierre agreed slowly, "if I can get out of the house without waking my family."

"Just wait until they go to sleep. Meet me here as soon after dark as you can," instructed Nanette.

While they talked softly together, Madame Busybody watched them suspiciously. "You two!" she snapped suddenly and sharply. "You had something to do with raising the gate, didn't you?"

"Oh, no. We didn't," Nanette and Jean Pierre denied quickly.

But the housewife still eyed them very suspiciously, and said to the woman beside her, "I think Nanette knows more about it than she wants to admit."

The day seemed long and the evening slow in coming. But at last bedtime came. Nanette lay wide-awake in her cupboard bed, waiting for Grandmere to fall asleep.

She waited a long time. Then very quietly she climbed out of bed, slipped into her clothes, and hurried out into the night.

Quietly Nanette padded up the lane in her soft slippers. Every cottage had its doors closed and its windows shuttered. She could easily see the familiar path, for the moon would soon rise. Already the sky in the east was growing lighter. However, she felt less lonely when she saw Jean

Pierre's small figure coming down the path from his house.

They reached the Lavoir at the same time. "Look," whispered Nanette, "It's full. Whoever lets out the water hasn't come yet."

They stood for a long minute looking out over the field and quiet surface of the Lavoir. Nothing stirred except an old goat with long beard and horns that Farmer Duquesne[2] had left to graze among the bushes nearby. Somehow Nanette felt safer with the goat nibbling there just as if the sun were shining.

"Let's hide, Jean Pierre, before anyone comes," Nanette said. "We don't want them to see us."

"Oh, no! Let's go home," whispered the little boy. "I'm scared. I don't care who lets the water out of the Lavoir. Let's go home."

The Lavoir, so friendly in the daylight, looked black and mysterious at night. Nanette herself almost wished she had stayed at home safe in bed.

Just then the moon cleared the trees, a large, bright, silvery moon—a very cheerful moon indeed. What a difference it made. Golden light seeped through the tree leaves and threw a glittering path straight across the Lavoir to where they stood.

"No, let's stay," Nanette said bravely. "Since we are here, we may as well find out who lets out the water."

Jean Pierre and Nanette sat down behind a bush and leaned against a boulder. Nothing moved, except Farmer

---

[2]Duquesne – dü kān′

215

Duquesne's goat nibbling, nibbling, and the golden trickle of water running out the overflow pipe.

The cousins settled more comfortably in their hiding place. They waited and waited, growing sleepier and sleepier. At last their eyes closed.

Out in the silvery moonlight the goat ate all the grass he could eat on one side of the Lavoir. He stood at the gate looking wistfully across the water to where the grass grew thick and green. After a moment he lowered his head. He hooked his horns under the gate and lifted.

Nanette woke suddenly to the sound of gushing water. There stood the old goat holding up the gate while the water gurgled merrily out of the Lavoir. In a minute he would be able to walk through the empty Lavoir to the good grass on the other side.

"Jean Pierre!" cried Nanette, "look at the old goat. He has raised the gate and let out the water. Chase him across and I'll shut the gate."

Jean Pierre jumped up and dragged the goat away. Nanette pushed the gate down again, and the water stopped running out of the Lavoir.

The children went home in the moonlight, very pleased with having solved the mystery of the empty Lavoir. "Won't everyone be surprised when we tell what we discovered," said Nanette when Jean Pierre started up his path. "No one will guess we were out here tonight finding out what really happened. How silly it was to think some child raised the gate. They shouldn't have been so suspicious of us."

But one person did know about it. Madame Busybody, the gossip, had extremely sharp ears. When she heard soft footsteps pattering by her house, she had gotten up. She peeped out the window and saw Nanette going by.

"Oho! So little Nanette steals out at night!" she said to herself. "So it is Nanette who raises the gate! I thought she and that little cousin of hers acted guilty. Well, tomorrow everybody shall hear of this. Yes!" Madame Busybody went back to bed, delighted to have some new gossip to tell the housewives tomorrow.

Very early the next morning Madame Busybody pinned on her best white cap and apron and went visiting. First she stopped at her nearest neighbor. "Good morning," she said. "Have you heard the latest news? Who do you suppose has been letting the water out of the Lavoir?"

"I cannot imagine," answered the neighbor.

"Well," said the gossip, "you'll never guess, so I'll tell you. It is none other than Nanette. With my own eyes I saw her pass my house late last night, when all good little girls were asleep in bed. Yes! Nanette steals out at night to raise the gate and cause trouble for all of us. I shall go now to tell her grandmere."

"Why, what a wicked child!" exclaimed the neighbor. "I'll go with you, but let us tell my neighbor first."

So they stopped at the next house and said to the housewife, "Have you heard the news? Nanette is the one who has emptied the Lavoir. We are on our way to tell her grandmere."

"I'll go with you," said the housewife. "But let us tell my neighbor first."

They stopped at every house in the lane to tell the news. Each housewife wanted to go along to see what Nanette had to say for herself. By the time they had reached Nanette's house, all the housewives who lived in the lane had gathered there, all eager to tell Grandmere about Nanette.

Grandmere came to the door when they knocked, and she acted very much surprised to see all her neighbors.

"Why, what goes on? A wedding?" she asked. They all looked at her very solemnly. "Or a funeral? What is it?"

"Let us talk to Nanette," said Madame Busybody.

"Nanette is a sleepyhead this morning," said Grandmere. "She hasn't gotten up yet."

"Ah, no wonder," said Madame Busybody. "We came to tell you why. It is your Nanette who steals out at night to raise the Lavoir gate. I saw her with my own eyes!"

"That is impossible," Grandmere exclaimed. "Nanette was fast asleep in her bed—she will tell you so herself!" She called Nanette.

Nanette came out, very sleepy-eyed.

"Nanette, did you go out last night?" Grandmere asked.

"Yes, I went out, but—" Before the girl could finish, Madame Busybody turned to the housewives.

"There!" she cried triumphantly. "You see! Nanette emptied the Lavoir. I told you so!"

All the housewives glared at Nanette. They all began talking angrily.

"No, no," Nanette shouted over the clamor. "The Lavoir is full of water this minute. Go and see for yourselves."

"I do not believe it," snapped Madame Busybody. "But we will go and see."

She led the way to the Lavoir, with all the housewives trailing after. And all the housewives' children too.

Soon they came to the Lavoir. Sure enough, full to the brim, the Lavoir reflected the blue sky like a mirror.

"There! You see!" said Nanette. "I didn't empty the Lavoir. But I can tell you who did. See that old goat over there. He did it with his horns. Jean Pierre chased him to the other side and I shut the gate. If we hadn't, the Lavoir would be empty this morning."

All the housewives glared at the goat. Then they began to smile at Nanette. "Good, clever Nanette. You have solved the mystery."

Only Madame Busybody did not smile, because now no one would believe her gossip. Everyone knew she had not seen Nanette empty the Lavoir. No one would believe anything she said after this.

As for the old goat, he kept nibbling away at the thick green grass. He paid no attention to the housewives glaring at him from across the water of the Lavoir.

*If Madame Busybody had done what this poem says, how might the story have turned out differently?*

# Kind Words

Kind hearts are the gardens,
   Kind thoughts are the roots,
Kind words are the flowers,
   Kind deeds are the fruits.

Take care of the gardens,
   And keep them from weeds.
Fill, fill them with flowers,
   Kind words and kind deeds.

—Henry W. Longfellow

*In the story, one goat caused a lot of trouble. Imagine one thousand goats—more or less!*

# The Goatherd

One day there reached me from the street
The sound of little trampling feet;
And through the dust and sunlight, I
Saw 'most a thousand goats go by.

The goatherd followed close behind:
He looked quite undisturbed and kind,
And Pablo said he knew him well,
And called him Señor Manuel.

His jacket was a shaggy skin,
And scarlet figures woven in
His blue zarape, made it gay
As though for a fiesta day.

221

His black eyes twinkled in the shade
That his broad-brimmed sombrero made;
And all his teeth were shiny bright
Like Mother's porcelain, and as white.

Before he went, he took a drink
Of something very good, I think,
For he held up the gourd he wore
To Pablo's lips—then drank some more.

I told him there had seemed to be
At least a thousand goats, and he
Just laughed and said—to make a guess—
There *were* a thousand, more or less!

—Grace Hazard Conkling

*"Comfort the feebleminded, support the weak,*
*be patient toward all men."* 1 Thessalonians 5:14

# I'm the Big Sister Now

## All About Amy

My mom and dad knew right away that God had made my sister Amy a special little girl. Part of her brain did not work because she did not get enough **oxygen** during birth. We call this kind of brain damage cerebral palsy[1]. Some people with cerebral palsy limp when they walk or have a hand that is crooked at the wrist so that they can't hold onto things. Some of them are a little hard to understand when they talk. Some others who can't walk can still **operate** their own wheelchairs. However, Amy is severely

---

[1] cerebral palsy – sə rē′ brəl pól′ zē

**handicapped**. She cannot sit up, use her hands, walk, talk, read, write, or do anything a normal child can do. She has always been in a wheelchair made just for her.

Even though she cannot do very many things, she is still a great sister, and I would like to tell you about her.

## *How I Feel About Amy*

Amy started out as my big sister. She was five when I came along. Of course, I did not know that she was different from any other big sister. I liked to lie near her. She made baby sounds like I did, and I felt happy and safe beside her.

After I grew out of my youth bed, I told my parents that the dark scared Amy, and she needed me close to her. Actually, I was the one who was afraid, so I started sleeping with Amy. When I had a bad dream or became scared of the dark, I just cuddled up to her, and we both went to sleep.

Now the dark doesn't scare me anymore, but I still like to be with Amy. In some ways I think she actually is better than other big sisters. My friends say their older sisters boss them around. Amy never tells me what to do, and she always listens when I talk to her.

Amy gets sick a lot. Once she was so sick we thought she might die. I know she won't live as long as I will, and that makes me sad. I wonder when she will die, and how.

It is lonely at night when Amy is in the hospital, and we all are glad when she comes home. When Amy is well, I don't worry about her.

I do not feel jealous when Mom and Dad spend so much time with Amy, because she can't help being sick. When she is okay, they do special things with me.

As I grow older, I get bigger, as most children do. But Amy does not grow very fast. At fourteen years she looks only five or six. I am nine, but I can hold Amy and even carry her if I am careful. Because I'm taller and stronger and can help Amy to feel happy and safe, Mom says I have become her big sister. Being her big sister makes me feel good inside too.

## How Others Feel About Amy

One time when I was little, Mom, Amy, and I went to the park. A man on a huge motorcycle pulled up to us. He had long, greasy hair and wore a jacket with the name of a gang on it. Mom looked around quickly, worried that he would cause trouble, but she couldn't see a policeman or anyone else around. But when the man got close, Mom saw he had tears in his eyes. He said, "Can I do anything for your little girl?" My mom felt greatly relieved and answered all his questions. Amy always seems to bring out the best in people.

Once when our family went somewhere a couple of rude girls started staring at Amy. I went over to Amy and hugged her.

Amy does not like people staring or pointing at her. We think it makes her uncomfortable. But we do not mind having people ask questions, because that shows they care and are interested. People usually say things like, "Was she born the way she is?" or "Can she walk or talk?" Sometimes they ask whether she is happy or sad when she makes loud noises. They ask why she always holds her mouth open.

I can answer most questions. She makes happy noises or sad ones depending on how she feels. She cannot close her mouth completely because of the way it was formed.

My family went to my grandma and grandpa's church last Christmas, and someone we didn't know said, "Merry Christmas, Amy." We couldn't figure out how he knew her. Then later we noticed that Amy's wheelchair had a name tag tied onto the handle. It made us feel good that people cared enough about Amy to include her.

Sometimes Amy and I go to the pool. She can float without a life jacket if people hold their hands under her head. Little children five or six years old will float her by keeping her head up out of the water and pulling her around the pool. Sometimes they argue over whose turn it is to float Amy. She laughs a lot while she floats, and smiles at the person pulling her. Mom sits right nearby so that she can help if Amy starts to slip under.

Amy started going to a special school when she was only a year old. All the children there are handicapped, but in different ways. Some of them can walk a little or play with toys by themselves. Some learn to feed themselves and to use the bathroom. The children who can use their hands learn sign language if they cannot talk. With the teachers' help, some children can paint pictures. The school has special exercise mats and balls in the classroom and a "standing board" that helps the boys and girls stand in front of a desk. Amy likes to play in a big playpen filled with styrofoam.

Teachers from other rooms like to visit Amy, especially when they feel sad or lonely. Amy makes people feel happy and important. She is very pretty, and usually smiles when you talk to her. Her eyes tell you how much she enjoys life. You think, *If she is not sad with all her handicaps, then I shouldn't be either, because I can do so many things.*

Amy is a good listener. You can tell her secrets, and you know she won't tell anyone. She will listen as long as you want to talk, without saying she's too busy or that what you are saying is silly. You always feel better after you talk to her.

Growing up with Amy makes me grateful for the many blessings I've been given. She has taught me and my family to be comfortable with anyone. I'm glad God made Amy a part of our family.

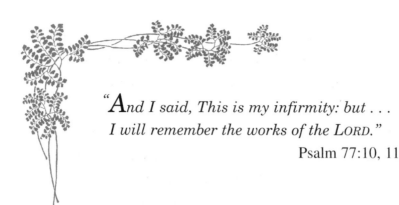

*"And I said, This is my infirmity: but . . .
I will remember the works of the LORD."*

Psalm 77:10, 11

# A Recollecting Day

Joyce put one foot on the bottom stair and counted *one, two, three, four, five.* Then she put her other foot on the next step and counted *one, two, three, four, five;* and so on all the way upstairs. She played this little counting game every afternoon when she went upstairs for her nap. Girls who have been sick for a long time must go upstairs very slowly.

Once upstairs, Joyce went to the little round window at the end of the hall and looked out. She loved the tiny **landscape** she could see from there. The river looked like a little brook with toy houses scattered beside it. Just then, a toy train puffed its way between two hills. It glided into the picture, then **receded** into the distance. Joyce liked to pretend the scene out the little window was a picture hanging on the wall there. Every time she came upstairs she tried to see something different in the picture.

Joyce waited until the distant smoke cleared away. Then she went to her room, eased into bed, and closed her eyes. She wished she could close her ears too. She heard Joanna romping in the yard with Rover. Joyce could hear her laughter and Rover's excited barking.

For a minute Joyce wished she could join them instead of lying in bed. But that wish receded, for almost at once a dozen different games rushed into her mind, begging to be played. Some days she tried to think of all the words she knew that began with *a*, then with *b*, and so on. She never had reached *z*. She always fell asleep before she got there, no matter how hard she tried to stay awake. Sometimes she tried to recall all the flowers or birds she knew. She pictured to herself their brilliant colors, sweet fragrances, or cheery songs. Sometimes she painted a make-believe landscape. She first thought of a blank sheet of paper, then splashed imaginary colors on it.

Today, however, Joyce decided against all of these games. Today would be a **recollecting** day. Not a long-ago-recollecting-day nor a last-week-recollecting-day, but an in-between-recollecting-day. She closed her eyes. The outside noise receded. She began.

She recalled a day soon after she came home from the hospital. (Joyce could not bear, even now, to remember those worst days in the hospital.) She had begun to feel

229

better by then, but **intensely** tired. Lying in bed made her tired. Looking at books became tiresome, and how tired she was of taking nasty medicine. Most of all, she hated looking endlessly at the long crack in the ceiling plaster that **extended** over her bed. All of which resulted in a very grouchy little girl.

Poor Mother sat there looking tired, too, though of course she didn't look cross as Joyce did. Just sad and intensely weary. At that awful point, Aunt Edith had breezed into the house. She took in the situation at a glance.

"Now listen, Martha," she told Mother, "you must get away for a little while or you'll be sick too. Drive my car over to Grandma's. Stay there and visit with her until time for Joanna to come home from school. I'll take care of **entertaining** Joyce and get John's lunch."

"Daddy's helping Uncle Allen fix his tractor and won't come home for lunch," Joyce said. The day already looked a little brighter to her. No one else could be quite so jolly and entertaining as Aunt Edith.

Mother protested at first. However, she really was very tired, and a day with Grandma sounded like such a treat. She had scarcely seen Grandma since Joyce became ill. So before long, Mother had departed, and Aunt Edith sat in an easy chair beside Joyce's bed. Her needle moved as fast as her tongue as she mended huge holes in Daddy's socks.

Somehow, though, not even Aunt Edith's entertaining chatter could get rid of Joyce's gloom that day. She kept thinking of Joanna at school. She thought of her twin getting ahead in their lessons so far that she could never catch up. She thought of Joanna growing taller than she, and fatter too—a tragic condition for twins who had always been exactly the same size. Suppose her illness extended into the future farther than the doctor had said! Nothing would ever be the same again even when she did get well. Right in the middle of Aunt Edith's most entertaining story, a very wet tear splashed down on the sheet.

"What is it, Joyce?" Aunt Edith asked anxiously. "Are you feeling worse again?"

"No, it isn't that." Joyce swallowed a sob and stared at the crack in the ceiling that she already knew by heart. "It's just everything all together, Aunt Edith. It's having to stay in bed and having to take medicine. It's getting behind in my lessons and missing birthday parties and everything else. I don't see why it had to be me that got sick."

"But surely you wouldn't want Joanna to be sick instead?" questioned Aunt Edith.

"No, of course not, but why should either of us have to get sick? Why couldn't we just go on as we did before? It seems to me, if God really loved people, He would not let them be sick at all."

"Shall I tell you why I think God let you be sick, Dear?" Aunt Edith asked. Joyce nodded her head.

"Well, you know, God has plans for people all the time. Some plans He has to throw away because nobody will help Him do them.

"Now I think God had a very special plan in mind one day. Out of all the people in the world, He chose you to carry out that plan for Him. But before you could carry out that plan, He had to teach you a lot of things. He couldn't just let you go dashing through life without ever noticing or being thankful for little, everyday things. He needs someone who is patient and can be kind to other poor, sick people.

"Most of all, He needs someone who knows the Bible; someone who loves Him very much. So, because He needed that kind of person, He let you be sick for a while. I'm sure He's hoping that you'll use this time to work on becoming the kind and patient and cheerful person He needs.

"Remember, you can never learn patience if everything goes just the way you like it to. You can never learn to be thankful until you know what it is like to do without things. You can never practice being cheerful if you always feel great. God let you get sick so you would learn to thank Him for every day that you feel better. He let you get behind Joanna in school to give you a chance to practice cheerfulness and patience and faith in His plan.

"God knows you will need all those things if you are going to carry out that special plan He has for you. Of course, you won't know what the plan is for a long time, but you can be getting ready.

"Now, I must run to the kitchen and see what I can find for our lunch. While I'm gone, I suggest that you ask God to help you accept His plan for you."

All that had been several months ago. Now Joyce looked at the little clock on her dresser. In ten more minutes she could join Joanna in the sunshine. Of course, she couldn't play any rough running games, but they loved to play dolls or school out on the screened back porch. She and her twin had no trouble entertaining themselves. "How much better that is," she said to herself, "than at first when I couldn't even get out of bed."

Joyce suddenly felt intensely thankful that she had remembered that day of Aunt Edith's visit. It had been the beginning of many good times for her. She had begun to notice little things in the landscape she had never seen before—the lovely pattern of clouds against the sky, the first tiny swelling of leaf buds on the maple tree, the swoop of swallows over the toolshed roof. She counted the number of times Mother came at her call without ever getting impatient, and wrote them down in a little notebook. She recorded the times Daddy remembered to wave when he passed her window, and the many days Joanna gave up playing in the snow after school to sit with her.

As these lists extended further down the pages in her notebook, Joyce stopped pitying herself. She invented little games she could play to keep herself entertained when alone, rather than calling for someone to come and play with her. Best of all, the thought of God's special plan for her always glowed in her heart.

# Others

Even though it's raining,
I don't wish it wouldn't.
That would be like saying
I think it shouldn't.
I'd rather be out playing
Than sitting hours and hours
Watching rain falling
In drips and drops and showers,
But what about the robins?
What about the flowers?

—Harry Behn

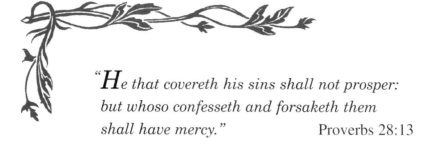

*"He that covereth his sins shall not prosper: but whoso confesseth and forsaketh them shall have mercy."* Proverbs 28:13

# Facing the Music

"Kent, what does 'facing the music' mean?" inquired Todd as his big brother entered the room.

"'Facing the music'? Who did you hear say that?"

"Our teacher. Today someone broke the window in the woodshed at school. When Miss Ross asked about it, no one said anything. Then she said it was the same as telling a lie if you did it but didn't speak up when she asked about it. I couldn't see how it could be telling a lie if you didn't say anything."

"Well, it is," said Kent. "That is the same as saying, 'I didn't do it' because your silence makes people think you didn't. You know the Bible says when someone in **authority** asks for information about something, you are guilty if you don't tell what you know. But what did she say about 'facing the music'?"

"She said if you are guilty but refuse to face the **consequences**, you will just keep quiet or run away from those consequences. She said it takes a brave person to face the music. But she didn't say what kind of music she was talking about," said Todd.

"Oh, that is just a saying," said Kent. "I don't know where it got started. But I know what it means. In fact, I remember when I first heard that saying. It was in a story I read when I was about your size. Do you want me to tell it to you?"

"Sure," said Todd. "Then maybe I'll find out what 'facing the music' means."

Here is the story Kent told:

A postmaster in a big city was working in his office one afternoon. He heard a faint knock on the door.

"Come in," he said.

The door eased open, admitting three dirty, ragged, little street **urchins**. They looked scared out of their wits.

"What may I do for you?" asked the postmaster in a deep voice of authority.

"Oh, sir, we done it, and—and—we are here to face the music," **stammered** the smallest of the boys.

"What did you do?" asked the postmaster, much surprised.

"Well, him and him,"—here the little fellow jerked his thumb toward the two other boys—"and me, and Beanie

and Scotty were playing Follow the Leader. Beanie was the leader, and he jumped over one of them mailboxes you have on the street fer people to put letters in.

"Then I tried to jump over it, but I didn't make it. The box tipped over. When it fell, the lock hit the curb and broke off. All the letters poured out in the street. We put 'em all back. Every one. And set the box up. But we couldn't fix the lock."

"Where is this box?" asked the postmaster.

"Corner of First and Willow. We knew right off we had done something awful, but we didn't mean to. So we was going to **vamoose**. Then we knew that wouldn't be right. So then we decided to put our names on the box and let you find us if you could. But we knew you'd never catch all five of us. So that wouldn't be fair either."

Suddenly one of the other urchins spoke up. "Lil' Buddy here said he was the one what knocked the mailbox over, so just put his name on it and leave the others off."

The third boy finally found his voice. "But Beanie said he was the leader and jumped over the box first. We'll stick together—all face the music or all vamoose.

"Then Scotty said that if we run off, someone would steal all them letters. So we knew we couldn't do that. The only thing left was to come and face the music."

"But we didn't all come," Lil' Buddy took up the tale. He didn't stammer now. "We left Beanie and Scotty at the box so that no one will snitch any letters. Them letters are safe with Beanie and Scotty. So him and him"—again the thumb

239

jerked toward the two other boys—"and me, come to tell you, and to take what's coming to us."

The postmaster looked at the three nervous little fellows. Then he smiled and said, "I wish I could tell you boys how great I think you are. Not many boys would be so honest as to take the blame for what they did when they could have gotten by without telling. Most boys wouldn't care if the letters did fall out of the box and get stolen. Not many would be so brave as to come and face the consequences as you have done."

By that time the scared looks had left the three little faces. The boys smiled in shy relief.

The postmaster came from behind his desk. His air of authority was gone. "I want to shake hands with such brave boys," he said. "God bless you—and Scotty and Beanie, too. Keep on being brave and honest, and you will go far toward being happy in this life. Facing the music is never easy; but that's soon over and done with. A guilty conscience and the fear of being caught can keep you miserable for years. Now you go and tell Scotty and Beanie what I said, and I'll send someone to take care of that box right away."

As the boys left the office, the postmaster heard one of them say, "See, I told you they wouldn't hang us."

"Well, that's the story that showed me what 'face the music' means," said Kent. "Do you think you understand it now?"

"Yes, I do," said Todd thoughtfully. "It means facing up

240

to the consequences of whatever you did that turned out wrong. Those little fellows were sure they would be punished for what they had done. But they didn't run away or even just wait to be caught. They went straight to the one in authority and confessed what they had done. And they didn't blame anyone else or act like what they had done wasn't so bad. I like that."

He was quiet for a long time. Then he said, "When I think how honest and brave those little fellows were, I guess I can face the music when I go to school tomorrow."

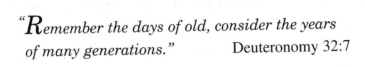

# Grandma's Memory Table

Shanna walked slowly into the kitchen, absent-mindedly chewing a fingernail. A frown had replaced her usual happy smile.

"Shanna, please don't chew your fingernails," Mother said, glancing up briefly from packing lunches. "What's bothering you?"

"It's Grandma," **blurted** Shanna. "I stopped in her room a minute ago like I always do before I go to school, and she just sits there. I tried to talk with her, but she wouldn't say much. She just nodded and smiled a little, like she didn't really see me."

Shanna's mother thought a moment. Then she said slowly, "We need to remember that Grandma just came from the hospital. She tires easily. More than that, she knows she will never be able to go back to her own house to live as she did after Grandpa died. She finds it very difficult to accept the fact that from now on she must depend on us to do everything for her. She feels like she is such a useless **burden**."

"I understand that, Mom," said Shanna. "But before she came here she laughed a lot and seemed so happy. Now she hardly smiles. Isn't she thankful that she can live with us and not have to work anymore?"

"Shanna," Mother spoke rather sharply, "don't you ever get the idea that Grandma should thank us for bringing her into our home. She did not choose to come here. She was **compelled** to come because she couldn't keep house any longer."

"Why would Grandma want to continue keeping house, at her age?" asked Shanna, in a puzzled voice. "As hard as she worked all her life, doesn't she feel she deserves a rest?"

"No, indeed," replied Mother. "Just think. For years and years her husband and children needed her. She cooked and cleaned and washed and ironed. She tended a big garden and canned and froze things. After Grandpa died and the children all left home, she spent many more years helping neighbors and church people and teaching Sunday school.

"Now since she can't do any of those things, no one needs her. You and I can't imagine how useless she feels. No wonder she sees herself as a burden to us. No wonder she finds it hard to stay cheerful."

"I never thought of all that," said Shanna slowly. "Poor Grandma. I wish I could think of something that would help her to feel happy."

Then a new thought popped into her mind. "Mom, do you suppose it would make her happier if she had more of her things here? Would she feel better if she weren't compelled to use our things all the time, but we could use some of her things?"

Mother's face lighted with interest. "A wonderful idea, Shanna. She deserves to have something of her own here. Let's both put our minds to this today. Grandma has lots of things in **storage**, but how could we ever hope to guess which of those things might make her happiest?"

"We should keep our ears open when we visit with her. Maybe she will say something that would give us an idea."

All day at school, Shanna thought about Grandma's possessions that she had helped pack and carry up to the garret in Grandma's old house. Dishes, quilts, chairs, pictures, vases—she could think of nothing that Grandma had seemed particularly attached to.

She **concocted** half a dozen questions to ask. One of them might make Grandma mention something she'd like to get out of storage. But she still hadn't thought of anything.

Mother, too, shook her head when Shanna got home from school.

After supper Shanna stopped by Grandma's room, and tapped on her open door. Grandma looked up from a photo **album** with her usual sweet smile. "Come in, Shanna. I'm sorry I didn't act very pleasant this morning."

"Oh, you weren't really cross, Grandma," Shanna declared, picking up a few loose pictures and leafing through them. "I must have stopped in at a bad time. You seemed so far away. You must have been thinking about something else."

"I was remembering another September long ago," said Grandma. "Grandpa had started making a special birthday present for me."

"In September? Why did he begin so early when your birthday comes in November?"

"Well, the present took many hours to build," explained Grandma, with a happy remembering look in her brown eyes. "He wanted to surprise me with it. Of course, I knew he was working on something; but I didn't know what."

"Didn't you ever want to peek?" asked Shanna.

"Of course I wanted to peek. I just could not imagine what he could be making. Sometimes I felt compelled to look, but I never did."

"What did he make?"

"A table," said Grandma.

"A table!" blurted Shanna.

"Yes, a big kitchen table made from the prettiest walnut wood I had ever seen." Grandma laughed at Shanna's look of surprise. "Oh, I know, it doesn't sound like a very exciting present to you. But nothing could have pleased me more. We had only a few pieces of furniture when we got married—no table at all. We made one by stacking wooden boxes together. Grandpa gave me a lot of birthday presents after that one, but none of them made me as happy as that walnut kitchen table."

Grandma paused and pulled out a faded picture from the album. "There it is. We called it our memory table," she said softly.

In the picture a very young-looking Grandma looked up from rolling out piecrust on a very ordinary-looking table.

"Please tell me more about it," begged Shanna. "Why did you call it your memory table?"

Grandma smiled that remembering smile again. "First you need to understand how I felt about that table. The beautiful wood and the fact that my new husband had spent so many loving hours making it for me made it extra special. We possessed so few pretty things that I wanted to keep it that way.

"However, we were compelled to use that table for just about everything. I cut out dresses on it. I bathed the baby on it. I kneaded bread and rolled out piecrusts on it. Grandpa doctored sick animals on it. We used it when we butchered. When the children grew older, that's where they did their homework. The boys—your daddy and his brothers—built things on it. One day something went wrong when your dad was working on a chemistry experiment. *Pooo-f-f-f!* You can still see the dark, burned patch that experiment left. And of course, I scratched it and spilled things on it myself.

"At first I got upset when someone marred my beautiful

birthday present. Trying to keep it nice became a real burden. Then Grandpa gave me a new thought. He said we were writing a family history right there on the table. Every scratch and dent and stain told a story, leaving a memory of those hard, but happy years."

"But you did eat on it too, sometimes, didn't you?" asked Shanna.

"Bless your heart. Of course, we did," answered Grandma with a laugh. "All of us liked to talk. What good times we had just talking together around that table!"

"What became of the table? Did you wear it out and get a new one when you had more money?"

"No indeed!" exclaimed Grandma. "When the girls got older, they wanted a nice one. And the boys said they'd pay for any table I wanted to pick out. I told them that table was just as strong as when Grandpa first made it. Yes, it looked pretty beat-up on top, but every one of those marks held a memory.

"They stored it away in the garret when I didn't need such a big table anymore. When I get to feeling better, I'm going to ask your dad to take us over to the old home place. I'll tell you about all those scratches and dents and stains in my memory table. That table is just like an album of my life when the family was all home yet.

"Oh, Shanna, I'm sorry I talked so much. Don't let me bore you with my ramblings."

"Grandma, you didn't bore me a bit," declared Shanna. "Now I must let you go to sleep." Shanna kissed her grandmother gently on the forehead, then went out and closed the door quietly behind her.

She fairly flew downstairs. "Mother! Daddy!" she blurted out, bursting into the living room. "I know what we can bring for Grandmother. Her memory table!" Shanna told them all about her conversation.

"The very thing!" exclaimed Mother. "We will put it in the kitchen and eat off it three times a day. That should make Grandmother happy."

And Daddy said, "I would love to eat off that old table again, myself. Tomorrow I will go out to the home place and get it out of storage."

One day soon after that, Shanna rushed upstairs. "Grandma," she panted, "can you come downstairs with me? I want to show you something."

As they reached the kitchen, Shanna said, "Now you must close your eyes. We have a surprise for you." And she led Grandma into the room and up to the table. "Now open."

Grandma opened her eyes. She stared at the table, then gasped. Stepping up to it she ran her thin wrinkled hand over its scratched and stained surface. "My memory table," she whispered in a trembling voice. "My dear memory table."

She looked at Shanna and the rest of the family. Tears shone in her eyes. "You planned this, didn't you, Shanna? You'll never know what it means to me."

Shanna slipped her hand into Grandma's and said softly, "Now you can tell us about all the memories written on this table, and maybe we will add a few of our own to it."

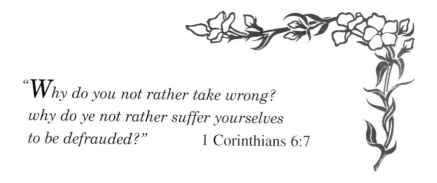

*"Why do you not rather take wrong?
why do ye not rather suffer yourselves
to be defrauded?"*     1 Corinthians 6:7

# Not Worth a Quarrel

[17] And Isaac departed thence, and pitched his tent in the valley of Gerar, and dwelt there.

[18] And Isaac digged again the wells of water, which they had digged in the days of Abraham his father; for the Philistines had stopped them after the death of Abraham: and he called their names after the names by which his father had called them. [19] And Isaac's servants digged in the valley, and found there a well of springing water.

[20] And the herdmen of Gerar did strive with Isaac's herdmen, saying, The water is ours: and he called the name of the well Esek; because they strove with him.

[21] And they digged another well, and strove for that also: and he called the name of it Sitnah.

[22] And he removed from thence, and digged another well;

and for that they strove not: and he called the name of it Rehoboth; and he said, For now the LORD hath made room for us, and we shall be fruitful in the land.

23 And he went up from thence to Beersheba. 24 And the LORD appeared unto him the same night, and said, I am the God of Abraham thy father: fear not, for I am with thee, and will bless thee, and multiply thy seed for my servant Abraham's sake.

25 And he builded an altar there, and called upon the name of the LORD, and pitched his tent there: and there Isaac's servants digged a well.

26 Then Abimelech went to him from Gerar, and Ahuzzath one of his friends, and Phichol the chief captain of his army. 27 And Isaac said unto them, Wherefore come ye to me, seeing ye hate me, and have sent me away from you?

28 And they said, We saw certainly that the LORD was with thee: and we said, Let there be now an oath betwixt [between] us, even betwixt us and thee, and let us make a covenant with thee; 29 That thou wilt do us no hurt, as we have not touched thee, and as we have done unto thee nothing but good, and have sent thee away in peace: thou art now the blessed of the LORD.

30 And he made them a feast, and they did eat and drink. 31 And they rose up betimes [early] in the morning, and sware one to another: and Isaac sent them away, and they departed from him in peace.

32 And it came to pass the same day, that Isaac's servants came, and told him concerning the well which they had

digged, and said unto him, We have found water. [33] And he called it Shebah: therefore the name of the city is Beersheba unto this day.

–Genesis 26

# Glossary

Every word that is in boldfaced type in your reader is in the glossary. With each word you will find the dictionary pronunciation and a definition. The definition given is for the way the word is used in the story in this book. Many of these words have other definitions. Most of the definitions also include a sentence with the word in it. That sentence is in *italic type.*

**accumulate** (ə kyü′ myə lāt) – to collect, pile up, or gather over time. *"It's funny how junk seems to accumulate in my room," said Johnny.* 187

**acquainted** (ə kwānt′ əd) – familiar with; knowing about. *I am acquainted with Mr. Johnson because I met him last year.* 120

**admired** (ad mīrd′) – respected and liked; approved of. *Everybody admired him for his courage and kindness.* 157

**advertising** (ad′ vər tīz ing) – to tell people about or ask people for. *She began advertising for a new baby-sitter.* 132

**affectionately** (ə fek′ shə nət lē) – lovingly. *The dog licked his master's face affectionately.* 90

**album** (al′ bəm) – a book that has blank pages for collecting photographs or other things. *I like to look at my parents' wedding album.* 244

**article** (ärt′ i kəl) – a short piece of writing that tells about something. *There was an article in the newspaper about the hurricane.* 89

**assembled** (ə sem′ bəld) – gathered together. *The men assembled to discuss what to do.* 98

**assistant** (ə sis′ tənt) – a helper. *Joyce is the teacher's assistant this week.* 76

**authorities** (ə thȯr′ ə tēz) – people in government who enforce the laws. *The authorities are looking for the person who robbed the bank.* 141

**authority** (ə thȯr′ ə tē) – having the right to give orders. *Our schoolteacher has authority over us.* 236

**bayed** (bād) – barked with long howls. *The dog bayed as he chased the coon through the river bottoms.* 87

**blurted** (blərt′ əd) – said suddenly, without thinking. *Before he thought what he was saying, James had blurted out the secret.* 242

**bonny** (bän′ ē) – attractive; fair; fine. *That mare of Jim's is a bonny horse.* 10

**briefly** (brēf′ lē) – in a short way; for a short while. *Allen stopped briefly to talk to Mr. Robinson.* 132

**buckskin** (bək′ skin) – a strong, soft leather made from the skin of a deer. *The trapper wore buckskin moccasins.* 25

**budge** (bəj) – move even a little. *We worked for three hours, but could not budge the large stone.* 189

**burden** (bər′ dən) – a duty; a heavy responsibility. *Grandma didn't want to be a burden to the family.* 243

**calico** (kal′ i kō) – a lightweight, printed cotton fabric. *I have a new calico dress.* 38

**capture** (kap′ chər) – to catch. *We played Capture the Flag at noon recess.* 84

**cautioned** (kȯ′ shənd) – warned. *Mother cautioned, "Be careful when you cross the log bridge."* 202

**chamber** (chām′ bər) – room. *Elijah slept in a small chamber built on top of the house.* 98

**chinked** (chingkt) – filled in the cracks between the logs of a log building with clay or other material. *Our new cabin was easier to keep warm after we chinked the cracks.* 5

**cobblestones** (käb′ əl stōnz) – rounded stones used long ago for paving streets. *The carriage wheels rattled over the cobblestones.* 177

**comical** (käm′ i kəl) – funny or amusing. *The monkey kept everybody laughing by doing comical tricks.* 157

**commotion** (kə mō′ shən) – much noise and confusion. *There was a lot*

---

**Pronunciation Key:** /ə/ but; /ä/ top; /yü/ use; /ər/ mother; /th/ thick; /<u>th</u>/ this; /ȯr/ corn; /ü/ boot; /u̇/ foot; /ȯ/ lost; /ȯi/ coin, toy; /är/ star; /au̇/ out; /zh/ measure; /ir/ deer; /er/ bear

*of commotion in the room when the teacher discovered the mouse in her drawer.* 90

**compelled** (kəm peld′) – forced. *The fear of losing the race compelled Paul to run even faster.* 243

**concocted** (kən käk′ təd) – made up; put together out of different things. *Mother concocted a soup out of the leftovers in the refrigerator.* 244

**consequences** (kän′ sə kwens əz) – results. *Lyndon found that the consequences of his wrong action followed him for a long time.* 237

**courageous** (kə rā′ jəs) – brave; having or showing courage. *Many courageous men and women have given their lives for Christ.* 202

**curtsy** (kərt′ sē) – a bow of greeting or respect made by girls. *To curtsy, keep one foot forward and bend your knees to lower your body a little.* 7

**dangled** (dang′ gəld) – hung loosely. *John dangled from the limb, then dropped to the ground.* 48

**darn** (därn) – mend by sewing back and forth across a hole or tear. *Some people darn their socks when they get a hole in them.* 37

**deceive** (di sēv′) – make someone believe what is not true. *Liars are always trying to deceive others.* 122

**decree** (dē krē′) – an order or command. *The king made a decree that all the world should be taxed.* 98

**denied** (dē nīd′) – to say that something is not true. *Todd denied that he knew anything about the broken window.* 213

**detective** (dē tek′ tiv) – person whose work is trying to solve crimes or find secret information. *A police detective found Tom's stolen car.* 140

**devoured** (dē vaùrd′) – ate or swallowed. *The hungry fox devoured the chicken, feathers and all.* 113

**donning** (dän′ ing) – putting on. *The men began donning their overcoats.* 202

**dwindle** (dwin′dəl) – to grow smaller and smaller or less and less. *Because she would not eat, her strength continued to dwindle.* 164

**eerie** ( ir′ ē) – making a person feel strange or mysterious; weird. *The wind blowing through the tunnel made an eerie sound.* 190

**elegant** (el′ i gənt) – beautiful and fine-looking. *"She has such elegant black hair," gushed Sue.* 83

**eluded** (ē lüd′ əd) – dodged or kept away from. *By fast running and quick dodging, Ray eluded the ball.* 54

**encrusted** (en krust′ əd) – covered with a crust or something like a crust. *After the ice storm, everything was encrusted with ice.* 195

**entertaining** (ent ər tān′ ing) – to keep interested. *Marlene was kept busy entertaining her small cousins.* 231

**excavated** (eks′ kə vāt əd) – dug. *The farmer excavated a place for his new pond.* 84

**excursion** (eks kər′ zhən) – a short pleasure trip. *The class went on an excursion to see the beautiful fall leaves.* 111

**existence** (ig zis′ təns) – life or state of being. *Some children believe in the existence of Santa Claus.* 75

**expedition** (eks pə di′ shən) – a trip or journey. *The children pretended they were on an expedition to Africa.* 62

**extended** (eks tend′ əd) – stretched out. *The fence extended along the edge of the meadow.* 231

**flounced** (flaúnst) – move with bouncy or jerky motions. *Sally flounced into the room, grinning broadly.* 115

**foolscap** (fülz′ kap) – a piece of writing paper. *Mother wrote directions to the mill on a piece of foolscap.* 6

**fowls** (faúlz) – birds. *Chickens, ducks, and hawks are kinds of fowls.* 153

**frantically** (fran′ tik lē) – in a very excited, fearful or worried way. *The family raced frantically for the storm shelter as the tornado approached.* 11

**future** (fyü′ chər) – the time to come. *No one knows the future except God.* 156

**gait** (gāt) – a way of walking or running. *The woman walked with a slow, shuffling gait.* 74

---

**Pronunciation Key:** /ə/ but; /ä/ top; /yü/ use; /ər/ mother; /th/ thick; /<u>th</u>/ this; /ȯr/ corn; /ü/ boot; /u̇/ foot; /ȯ/ lost; /ȯi/ coin, toy; /är/ star; /au̇/ out; /zh/ measure; /ir/ deer; /er/ bear

**galls** (gȯlz) – swellings in a plant. *We used oak galls soaked in water to make ink.* 6

**garret** (gar′ ət) – a room just under the roof of a house; attic. *Grandmother used to store lots of interesting things in the garret.* 46

**glared** (glerd) – stared angrily. *Sharon glared at her pesky little sister.* 212

**glistened** (glis′ ənd) – shone brightly with reflected light. *The sunlight glistened on the surface of the lake.* 111

**gratitude** (grat′ ə tüd) – thankfulness; appreciation. *The children showed their gratitude by writing a thank-you note.* 38

**handicapped** (hand′ i kapt) – having a physical or mental disability. *Many handicapped children go to special schools.* 224

**humor** (hyü′ mər) – state of mind; mood. *Tom was in good humor when he came home from school.* 122

**hundredfold** (hənd′ rəd fōld) – multiplied by one hundred. *The seed we planted increased a hundredfold.* 153

**infirmity** (in fər′ mə tē) – a weakness or sickness. *Grandma's infirmity kept her from going upstairs or out-of-doors.* 228

**inhabitants** (in hab′ ə tənts) – people or animals living in a certain place. *All of the little inhabitants of the forest were afraid of the hawk.* 63

**inkwell** (ingk′ wel) – a container in a desktop to hold ink. *You probably do not have an inkwell on your desk at school.* 6

**instinct** (in′ stingt) – something that God put into animals that makes them know what to do. *The rabbit knew by instinct that the fox was its enemy.* 53

**intensely** (in tens′ lē) – very. *Wilbert is intensely interested in cars.* 231

**investigating** (in ves′ ti gāt ing) – looking into to find out the facts. *The police are investigating the accident.* 180

**irritably** (ir′ ət ə blē) – angrily. *Joanne spoke irritably when she discovered what John had done.* 212

**laboratory** (lab′ rə tȯr ē) – room or building where scientific work is done. *In his laboratory, Mr. Salk developed a new way of treating disease.* 104

**landscape** (land′ skāp) – a scene of the land of an area or a picture of such a scene. *Lou painted a picture of a rugged mountain landscape.* 228

**linen** (lin′ ən) – fabric made of fibers from the flax plant. *Mother has a new linen tablecloth.* 178

**loped** (lōpt) – walked with long, swinging steps. *The horses loped across the plain.* 87

**lurked** (lərkt) – stayed hidden, ready to spring out and attack. *Dangerous animals lurked in the dense underbrush.* 52

**mansion** (man′ shən) – very large house. *The governor lives in a mansion in the town.* 46

**mental** (men′ təl) – done in the mind. *Cindy has always found mental arithmetic hard.* 103

**moisture** (mȯis′ chər) – wetness. *I can't get this paper to burn—it has too much moisture in it.* 153

**morsel** (mȯr′ səl) – small bit of food. *The beggar was glad for the morsel he received from the rich man.* 121

**motive** (mō′ tiv) – the reason a person does something. *I'm not sure what his motive was for lying to me.* 21

**muzzle** (məz′ əl) – the mouth, nose, and jaws of a dog, fox, or other animal. *The coyote pointed his muzzle to the sky and howled.* 89

**numb** (nəm) – without feeling; not able to feel. *My face turned numb where the snowball hit it.* 195

**nuzzled** (nəz′ əld) – touched with the nose. *The horse nuzzled Melanie gently.* 89

**obstruction** (əb strək′ shən) – something that is in the way. *An obstruction in his throat made it hard for him to swallow.* 189

**occupied** (äk′ yü pīd) – took up or filled. *The back row was occupied by five little sleepy-eyed girls.* 134

**operate** (äp′ ə rāt) – to run or work a machine. *Shawn is learning to operate a chain saw.* 223

---

**Pronunciation Key:** /ə/ but; /ä/ top; /yü/ use; /ər/ mother; /th/ **thick**; /<u>th</u>/ **this**; /ȯr/ corn; /ü/ boot; /u̇/ foot; /ȯ/ lost; /ȯi/ coin, toy; /är/ star; /au̇/ out; /zh/ measure; /ir/ deer; /er/ bear

**oxygen** (äk′ si jən) – the air we need to breathe to stay alive. *If we don't get enough oxygen, we may become ill or die.* 223

**parable** (par′ ə bəl) – short story about everyday things that has a spiritual meaning. *Jesus would often tell a parable to illustrate a truth He was teaching.* 153

**parched** (pärcht) – with the natural moisture removed. *My throat is so parched; I hope we soon find water.* 25

**pause** (pȯz) – a brief stop in speaking, reading, or activity. *He had to pause to catch his breath.* 103

**permanent** (pər′ mə nənt) – long lasting; meant to stay without changing. *By now, you have many of your permanent teeth.* 197

**petition** (pə tish′ ən) – a request or prayer. *He sent a petition to the king to help him.* 98

**pier** (pir) – dock; long flat surface built out over the water's surface. *Ronnie guided the boat in beside the pier.* 105

**preferred** (pri fərd′) – Liked or wanted better than. *I would have preferred to have a newer book than this one.* 134

**prongs** (prängz) – the pointed ends of a fork, deer antlers, etc. *Be careful—the prongs on that hay rake are sharp!* 171

**prospect** (präs′ pekt) – the possibility of something to come. *The prospect of a good night's sleep cheered the travelers.* 25

**protested** (prə test′ əd) – spoke out against. *He really protested when we said we were all going with him.* 140

**quills** (kwilz) – large feathers from a duck or goose tail, sharpened and used for writing. *The schoolmaster insisted that we keep our quills sharpened.* 6

**quivered** (kwiv′ ərd) – shook with trembling movements. *The oak leaves quivered in the early morning breeze.* 113

**ramp** (ramp) – a road, walk, or other area that slants from a lower place to a higher place. *We used a wooden ramp to get into the upstairs of the barn.* 164

**receded** (ri sēd′ əd) – to move backward. *After several days, the floodwaters slowly receded.* 228

**recollecting** (rek ə lekt′ ing) – remembering. *Grandmother fell silent, recollecting that long-ago day.* 229

**recommendation** (rek′ ə men dā shən) – a letter or something else that recommends something or a person. *John brought a recommendation from his last employer that said he was a good worker.* 134

**resisted** (rē zist′ əd) – fought against. *Peter resisted the temptation to peek at Jeremy's answers.* 76

**resolved** (rē zȯlvd′) – decided or determined. *Tom resolved to do his chores without being reminded.* 19

**routine** (rü tēn′) – regular way of doing something. *Jim has a routine for doing his chores.* 188

**scientist** (sī′ ən təst) – Someone who studies God's creation. *The scientist was studying various kinds of fish.* 104

**scorched** (skȯrcht) – burnt slightly. *Jerry scorched his hands while putting out the fire.* 156

**scuttled** (skət′ əld) – ran quickly; scurried. *Jolene scuttled out of the way when she saw the sled coming down the hill toward her.* 53

**secluded** (si klüd′ əd) – away from others; cut off from view; hidden. *We spent our two weeks off at a secluded cabin on an island.* 143

**seeped** (sēpt) – leaked through small openings. *Rain seeped in through the cracks in the wall.* 212

**seldom** (sel′ dəm) – not very often. *We seldom see her since she moved.* 163

**serenely** (sə rēn′ lē) – peacefully, calmly, and quietly. *Instead of crying out in fear, she answered us serenely.* 202

**shanks** (shanks) – legs. *You'll just have to use your own shanks this time because I don't have time to take you.* 202

**siphon** (sī′ fən) – a tube that is part of a clam's body. The clam uses it for taking in or shooting out fluids. *Clint picked up the clam by its long siphon.* 65

---

**Pronunciation Key:** /ə/ but; /ä/ top; /yü/ use; /ər/ mother; /th/ thick; /<u>th</u>/ this; /ȯr/ corn; /ü/ boot; /u̇/ foot; /ȯ/ lost; /ȯi/ coin, toy; /är/ star; /au̇/ out; /zh/ measure; /ir/ deer; /er/ bear

**smother** (sməth′ ər) – to keep from getting enough air to breathe. *We felt as if we would smother as we lay hidden in the hay.* 164

**squatted** (skwät′ əd) – crouched close to the ground. *The rabbit squatted in the clump of grass, hoping the fox would not see it.* 53

**stammered** (stam′ ərd) – spoke in an unsure way or in a nervous or embarrassed manner. *"I—I came to tell you—to tell you I'm sorry," stammered Ellis.* 237

**storage** (stȯr′ ij) – the condition of being stored. *My books are in storage, until I have a place for them in my house.* 244

**stowaway** (stō′ ə wā) – person who hides on a plane, ship, or other vehicle to get a free, secret ride. *The ship's captain was very unhappy when he discovered the stowaway.* 20

**superior** (sə pir′ yər) – higher than or better than something or someone else. *People who act superior toward others are not pleasing God.* 19

**supplication** (səp lə kā′ shən) a prayer asking something of God. *God heard Ezra's supplication for Israel.* 98

**supporting** (sə pȯrt′ ing) – holding up. *The old man walked slowly, supporting himself with a cane.* 62

**surmised** (sər mīzd′) – guessed. *We surmised that they had gone shopping because they took the checkbook along.* 142

**suspiciously** (səs pish′ əs lē) – doubtfully. *Mother looked at Anne suspiciously. "Are you telling the truth?" she asked.* 212

**sycamore** (sik′ ə mȯr) – tree with large leaves and smooth bark that often grows near water. *The raccoon climbed that big sycamore down by the creek.* 111

**tallow** (tal′ ō) – fat from cows or other animals that is used to make candles or soap. *Grandmother used tallow from cattle and from bears to make soap.* 45

**tedious** (tē′ dē əs) – tiring; long and difficult. *Adoniram Judson found that making a dictionary in an unwritten language is tedious work.* 157

**temptation** (tem tā′ shən) – something that makes a person want to do wrong. *John had to resist the temptation to get angry when Tim called him a name.* 155

**terrified** (ter′ ə fīd) – very frightened. *Emily was terrified when the neighbors' big dog barked at her.* 61

**thicket** (thik′ ət) – place where bushes, brush, and trees make a thick clump. *The rabbit found shelter in a small thicket.* 84

**trek** (trek) – a long, slow journey. *The pioneers faced many hardships on their trek through the wilderness.* 8

**urchins** (ər′ chənz) – mischievous youngsters. *Years ago, many little urchins played on the streets of London.* 237

**urgently** (er′ jənt lē) – strongly and seriously and quickly. *"Come quickly!" said Mother urgently. "There's been an accident."* 142

**vamoose** (və mūs′) – to leave quickly. *"We're going to have to vamoose if we are going to get home on time."* 239

**venison** (ven′ ə sən) – deer meat. *We had venison for supper the day after Father went hunting.* 27

**venture** (ven′ chər) – to go even though there is some risk. *After praying about it, we decided to venture into the forest to the west.* 179

**vibration** (vī brā′ shən) – a rapid shaking. *The vibration of the engine caused the bolts to come loose.* 191

**wharf** (whȯrf) – dock; long platform built over the water. *John walked out on the wharf while he waited for the boat to come.* 103

**whimper** (whim′ pər) – to make low crying or whining sounds. *The trapped dog began to whimper in fear and pain.* 196

**windfalls** (wind′ fȯlz) – trees blown down by the wind. *We had to work our way around many windfalls as we went through the forest.* 26

**windrows** (wind′ rōz) – long, narrow rows of hay (or something else) formed by raking or by the wind. *The children watched as Daddy raked the hay into long windrows around the field.* 169

---

**Pronunciation Key:** /ə/ but; /ä/ top; /yü/ use; /ər/ mother; /th/ thick; /th̲/ this; /ȯr/ corn; /ü/ boot; /u̇/ foot; /ȯ/ lost; /ȯi/ coin, toy; /är/ star; /au̇/ out; /zh/ measure; /ir/ deer; /er/ bear

# Acknowledgements

**Artist:** Michelle Beidler and others

**Cover artist and design:** Michelle Beidler and David Miller

**Editorial committee:** Jennifer Crider, Keith E. Crider, James Hershberger, Sadie Schrock

"A Boy's Song," by James Hogg.

"A Foxy Father," adapted from "Father Domino," from *Stories for Children and How to Tell Them,* courtesy of J. Berg Esenwein.

"A Recollecting Day," adapted by permission of Herald Press, from "A Remembering Day," by Edna Beiler, from *Words of Cheer,* 1950.

"Autumn Fires," by Robert Louis Stevenson.

"Banananananananananana," by William Rossa Cole. ©1977 William Rossa Cole.

"Bread Making," by E. L. M. King.

"Bridges Beyond," © 2001 Christian Light Publications, Inc., Harrisonburg, VA. All rights reserved.

"Burro with the Long Ears," from *Navajo Indian Poems,* transcribed by Hilda Faunce Wetherhill.

"Cabbages to Calves to Cows," adapted from "Dirk's Holiday," by Caroline D. Emerson.

"Candle-Making Time," adapted from "Candle-Making at the Turners," by Gertrude Stone and M. G. Fickett, adapted.

"Choosey Chick," adapted from "The Lost Boy," by Mabel Leigh Hunt.

"Chums" by Arthur Guiterman.

"Duck's Ditty," by Kenneth Grahame.

"Facing the Music," by Ruth Hobbs.

"Farewell to the Farm," by Robert L. Stevenson.

"First Day of Partridge School," adapted from "A Day With a Partridge Family," by Ernest Thompson Seton.

"Grandma's Memory Table," adapted from "The Memory Table," from *Sunshine Magazine,* by Jane Mcbride Choate.

"If it Hadn't Been for Buster," adapted from "Thanks, Little Bear," by Frank Kavanaugh.

"I'm the Big Sister Now," by Michelle Emmert. Copyright ©1989 by Michelle Emmert. Adaptation reprinted by permission of Albert Whitman & Company.

"In Spite of Lions," Daniel 6: 10-23, from the KJV Bible.

"Kind Words," by Henry W. Longfellow.

"Little Horse," by Elizabeth Coatsworth.

"Long before Tractors," adapted from "Hay is Made of Flowers," from *The New Outlook,* by Mary Quayle Innis.

"Nature's Sewing," Author Unknown.

"Neighborhood Needle," adapted from "The Neighborhood Needle," by Zelia Walters. Adaptation © 2001 Christian Light Publications, Inc., Harrisonburg, VA. All rights reserved.

"Neighboring," by Christina Rosetti.